Combat Conditioning

Functional Exercises for Fitness and Combat Sports

by Matt Furey

Matt Furey Enterprises, Inc.
10339 Birdwatch Dr., Tampa, Florida 33647, USA

Other Matt Furey Books and Courses – available at www.mattfurey.com:

Combat Conditioning Book

Kick Ass – Take Names…
Confessions of a Fitness and Fighting Guru

Matt Furey Inner Circle

Gama Fitness

The Furey Fat Loss System CD

Combat Conditioning Videos

Combat Cardio CD

Extreme Flexibility Secrets of The Chinese Acrobats

Combat Stretching

Combat Abs Book

The Secret Power of Handstand Training

Farmer Burns Catch Wrestling Home Study Course

Farmer Burns 1914 Classic –
Lessons in Wrestling & Physical Culture

Street Grappling

Neck Cranks

The Martial Art of Wrestling

Combat Training – The Road to China

How To Hook A Heavyweight Without Flopping to the Guard

How To Escape Any Submission Hold – Volume One

How To Cut Weight For Wrestling Without Losing Strength

Shuai-chiao Takedown Tactics for Grapplers

Mongolian Grappling Secrets Revealed – Two Videos

How To Use Your Feet To Score Takedowns

How to Eliminate Carpal Tunnel Syndrome within 30 Days

Magnetic Mind Power

Unrevealed Secrets of Man by George F. Jowett

Chuang Shang de Gong Fu

How to Make $1,000,000 (One Million) per Year (or More)
As A Personal Trainer or Fitness Professional

Disclaimer

The exercises and advice contained within this book may be too strenuous or dangerous for some people, and the reader(s) should consult a physician before engaging in them.

The author and publisher of this book are not responsible in any manner whatsoever for any injury which may occur through reading and following the instructions herein.

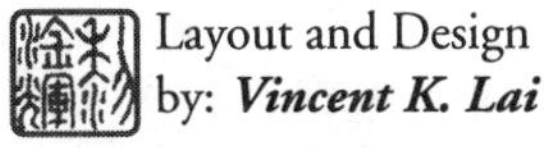
Layout and Design
by: ***Vincent K. Lai***

To

Karl Gotch

Thanks for all your help.

About the Author

Matt Furey is a native of Carroll, Iowa. He began competing in swimming and wrestling when he was eight years old – and through dedicated practice, became a champion in each sport.

In 1981, Furey was the state runner-up in the Class 3A Iowa High School State Wrestling Championships at 167-pounds. He attended The University of Iowa from 1981-1984, where he wrestled for Olympic Gold medalist, Dan Gable, and was a member of three national championship teams.

In the fall of 1984, in order to help rebuild a doormat wrestling program, Furey transferred to Edinboro University of Pennsylvania, and in 1985 he won the NCAA II national title at 167-pounds, defeating two-time California state champion, Howard Lawson, in the finals. While at Edinboro he was coached by Mike DeAnna and two-time Olympic Gold Medalist Bruce Baumgartner.

In February of 1987, Furey opened a training business for wrestlers and fitness enthusiasts. Most of the high school wrestlers he trained went on to wrestle in college.

Furey began studying various martial arts in 1990 and immediately saw the physical, mental and philosophical links these arts had with wrestling. This lead to the publication of his first book and videos in 1996, entitled, The Martial Art of Wrestling.

In 1996, Furey began competing in the ancient Chinese grappling art of Shuai-Chiao, the oldest style of kung fu. Furey's teacher, Dr. Daniel Weng, a national champion from Taiwan, and a ninth-degree black belt, guided Furey to three national titles – then over Christmas of 1997, Dr. Weng brought two U.S. teams to Beijing, China, to compete in the world championships. In Beijing, Furey won the gold medal at 90 KG (198-pounds), and was the only non-Chinese to win a title. In addition, Furey's world title was historic because it marked the first time that an American had won a gold medal in any world kung fu competition held in China.

In 1999, Furey traveled to Tampa, Florida to train under the legendary Karl Gotch. Several months later Furey moved his family from California to Tampa, Florida, so he could train with Gotch full-time. Gotch taught Furey a treasure trove of knowledge on conditioning as well as the real professional style of wrestling, known as catch-as-catch-can (catch wrestling).

Furey quickly excelled as a catch wrestler, earning him the covers of ***Grappling*** and ***Martial Arts Illustrated.*** ***Grappling*** magazine dubbed Furey, The King of Catch Wrestling – and in the book ***Grappling Masters***, Furey is one of 22 elite world class grapplers who are interviewed and featured.

In addition to the ***Martial Art of Wrestling*** and the international best-selling ***Combat Conditioning***, Furey's other best-selling books include ***Combat Abs*** and ***No B.S. Fitness***. Furey also has several best-selling courses, including: ***Combat Stretching***, ***Gama Fitness***, ***Magnetic Mind Power*** and ***The Farmer Burns Catch Wrestling Video Course***.

Furey publishes a FREE daily e-mail newsletter on his website at **www.MattFurey.com** that all are encouraged to sign up for. And he has an exclusive member's only website at **www.MattFureyInnerCircle.com**.

Furey writes a monthly column for ***Bodyguard*** and has been featured in ***GQ***, ***Black Belt***, ***Grappling***, ***Inside Kung Fu***, ***Martial Arts & Combat Sports***, ***Blitz***, ***Martial Arts Illustrated*** and many other publications throughout the world.

Along with his wife, Zhannie, Furey has two children, a son Frank, and a daughter, Faith. As a family they travel back and forth between their two homes in Florida, and Hainan Island, China.

Are You In Condition?

Take the following test:

1. Do you have trouble carrying your groceries or doing other mundane tasks?
2. Is your waistline bulging and your energy plummeting?
3. Do you feel old?
4. Do you have trouble sleeping at night?
5. Do you wear clothes that hide the way you look?
6. Do you feel you're under heavy stress?
7. Do you fell depressed or down?
8. Can you do 200 Hindu squats without stopping?
9. Can you do a handstand?
10. Do you have lower back and/or neck pain?
11. Are you stiff?
12. Are your muscles sore even though you don't exercise?
13. Do you feel tired throughout the day?
14. Do you feel like you have no control over your life?
15. Do you get sick easily?

If you answered yes to any of these questions, then
Combat Conditioning
is for you!

Important: Come to my website at **www.MattFurey.com** and give me your name and e-mail address. In return I promise to send you a free fitness tip every single day. My tips will keep you focused, informed and inspired. And they will entertain you beyond belief. For an example of the kind of material I will send you, check out pages 30 and 134 in this book. ***M.F.***

Will You Be Next?

Dear Matt,

Your ***Combat Conditioning*** and ***Gama Fitness Courses*** have given me a step by step guideline for achieving my goals. Last Christmas I weighed 377 lbs., as of August 12th my body weight is down to 239 lbs. and I lost over 20" on my waist!! My body fat is down to 18%. Imagine how good I felt when I could walk into a department store and buy a large shirt instead of a 5x shirt, 36" jeans instead of 58" jeans. Not only have I lost wait on your plan, but I also improved on my conditioning. I perform 500 Hindu Squats without stopping after a spinning class 3x a week! My Dead Lift has also gone up from 375 lbs. to 495 lbs. for 3 reps.!!! Your accolades as a wrestling and fitness guru will go unprecedented!!! I can't thank you enough.

Robert Lucarelli
Altamonte Springs, FL

Before

Robert Lucarelli weighing in at an out of shape 377lbs.

After

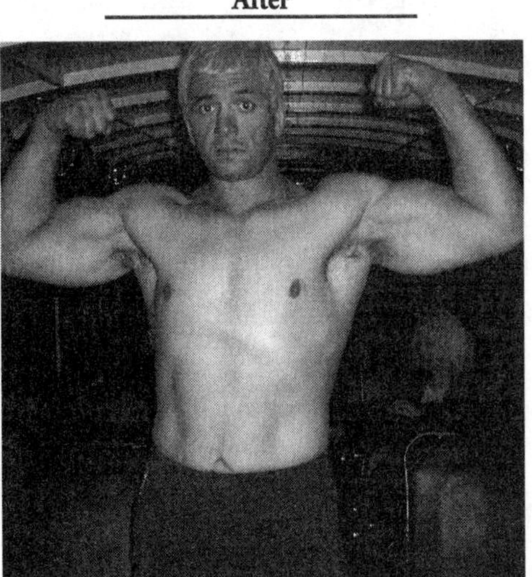

Robert weighing in at lean and fit 239lbs.

To discover more about the advanced program of ***Combat Conditioning*** that Bob Lucarelli followed, go to **www.Gama-Fitness.com**

*Send before and after photos and testimonials to **matt@mattfurey.com**. Maybe, like Bob, you'll be featured in the next edition of this book.*

This Book Is For You!

The book you now hold in your hands is for anyone who wants to improve upon his or her current level of fitness. It's for men, women and children. It's for business people and regular folks who simply want to get in shape. It's for combat athletes who want to improve their performance. It's for anyone who wants to follow the road to functional fitness.

Listed below are some of the many benefits you will experience as a result of studying and applying the exercises in ***Combat Conditioning.***

1. Your lower and upper back will be much stronger and more flexible, and your neck will be a bundle of pain free muscle.
2. Bulging waistline and excess flab will disappear.
3. Functional strength, flexibility and endurance will increase so much we can't even put a percentage on it, but let's just say 500% for starters.
4. You'll have less stress, better digestion and improved circulation.
5. You'll sleep better.
6. You'll have nerves of steel and a mind that can focus like a laser.
7. You'll have an exercise program that you can follow at home or on the road.

> *Great men breathe from their feet, average men breathe from their throats.*
>
> – ***Chuang Tzu***

Introduction

From the time I was 13 years old I have been keenly interested in learning the best ways to get in condition for sports. At that time I began training three days a week, using only one exercise, the clean and push press. In six weeks I noted some amazing changes in my physical appearance. And to a certain extent, the new muscles helped me perform better in the sports I was involved in: football, wrestling and swimming.

A year later, though, I began to train differently. After reading a number of books on bodybuilding, I believed the authors knew what they were talking about. The exercises they recommended with barbells, dumbbells and machines were not only designed to give me a better physique, but I was told they would make me a better athlete. I'm sorry to report that I wasted my time with those exercises.

When I was 15, I met a guy, Joe, who was about eight years older than me. Joe did 1000 pushups a day and ran like a deer. He was in incredible shape and after talking to him I began doing hundreds of pushups a day. At the time (1979), I noted that many of the top professional boxers did not lift weights. Instead, they concentrated on pushups, situps and other calisthenics. Like Joe, the pushups I began doing helped me get into better condition, but they were not the complete answer I was looking for and needed.

Throughout the rest of my high school career I continued to do bodybuilding exercises but the thing I noticed about them is that they didn't really give me functional strength and endurance. In the back of my mind, however, I knew that there had to be exercises without weights that were better than anything else I was doing. At times I came across them, but because "no one" else was doing them and no one could really explain to me why they were superior, I didn't stay with them for long.

Some of the most functional exercises I came across in my days as a high school and collegiate wrestler were pushups, free squats, situps, dips, pullups and handstand pushups. In addition, I found exercises like walking on my hands to be a tremendous upper body conditioner that also improved my balance and coordination.

In regard to the squats, I'll never forget the time during the winter of 1980, when my mother gave me an article that talked about dancers and how they built amazing strength and explosiveness in their thighs. Free squats, done in high numbers, were the key. That evening when I was doing my exercises, I began to incorporate the squats. I did 100 at a time, once per day.

Two weeks later I was wrestling in a tournament against a guy who had beaten me three times before. In a match six weeks earlier, he soundly defeated me. But he would not be facing the same person when I shook hands with him this time. I felt like I had springs in my legs. Every move I tried felt incredibly explosive. To the shock of my opponent, I won the match.

Amazingly enough, I never made the connection between the squats I had done for two weeks and the results of that match. Instead of continuing on with the daily squats, I did them every once in awhile. Big mistake.

When I got to the University of Iowa to begin my collegiate wrestling career I noticed that the best wrestler on the team, Ed Banach (a 3x NCAA champion and 1984 Olympic gold medalist), did not follow the same weight training routine that the others did. He followed a routine that consisted of calisthenics. The other wrestlers on the team laughed at the routine Ed followed. They felt it was "outdated."

One day when I began doing the free squats again, one of the other wrestlers looked at me and laughed. "What are you doing that for?" he asked. "Why use your own body weight when you can add more weight with a barbell or a machine?"

Oh how I wish I would have ignored that guy. I was getting in touch with the key to superior conditioning, and I let him talk me out of it. In the long run though, I have found that many of the mistakes I made in my earlier days have turned into a blessing. If I had never followed all the other routines, how would I truly know what is best for me?

In April of 1999, I was fortunate to meet Karl Gotch, a 1948 Olympian from Belgium, and the real brains behind the contents of this book. At 75 years of age, Karl, known as "The God of Wrestling" in Japan, showed me, in spite of my national and world title, that, in terms of conditioning, I had a long way to go to. Karl helped me understand that my 36-year old body, a body that many people considered to be highly athletic... was in fact, stiff, weak and in many ways, non-functional.

From that moment my life has never been the same. I was so impressed with what I was learning, not only about conditioning, but about the lost art of catch-as-catch-can wrestling, that I moved my wife and family from California to Florida, so that I could learn from Karl on a regular basis. Within a relatively short period of time, my strength, endurance and flexibility took a big leap forward.

"Imagine if I had you when you were 14 or 15," said Karl. "Imagine if you started learning these methods that long ago. With your desire and work ethic, there's no saying how far you would go."

Each day I work on the exercises contained in this book and each week I see improvements in my overall fitness and combat skills. The publication of ***Combat Conditioning*** represents my fervent desire to bring what Karl has taught me to those who have the eyes and ears for it.

If you feel something stirring inside your soul as you read this, you're ready to begin. Devote at least 15 minutes each day to the exercises in this book, and watch your life change for the better.

Begin at a pace that is in line with your current fitness level and make adjustments as you progress. As I tell my students, Rome cannot be built in a day... but it can be built.

Best of luck to you.

M.F.

Opening Instructions and Comments

Physical Condition — The exercises contained in this book are for people who are healthy. They can be done by men and women. Kids can do them as well, and so can people in their 40's, 50's and beyond, provided, of course, that their health is good and they have no orthopedic problems.

Exercise Periods — As a general statement, you'll want to devote 15 minutes per day to the exercises contained herein. In the beginning, 15 minutes may be more than some people can handle. Many people I have trained could not do 25 Hindu squats or five Hindu pushups when they began. This is understandable and if you are this type of person, begin slowly and coax yourself along to greater levels of fitness.

The Most Important Exercises — The most important exercises are what I call THE ROYAL COURT: Hindu Squats, Hindu Pushups and the back bridge. For those who are not physically able to do these three exercises, adapt and improvise. Find out what you can do, even if it is sitting for a minute in the wall chair or holding yourself in pushup position. Make a commitment to improve your health and stick to a daily program. As your condition improves, give yourself more to do, not less. The more time you put into your program, the more benefits you will receive. Many people will be able to do THE BIG THREE when they begin, but not very well. This should not stop you one bit. When I first began training in these exercises my form was far from perfect ... and I'm still making improvements. If you wait until your form is perfect, you'll be waiting forever. The main thing is that you BEGIN.

Minimum and Maximum — I have given a minimum number of repetitions or a time frame for some of the exercises. If you cannot do the minimum, do not hold this against yourself. Do what you can and keep trying. That's the key. A maximum number is generally not given as the sky is the limit in terms of what the human body can do. For example, Karl Gotch once did 9001-straight Hindu squats. It took him four and a half hours. On the eve of the new millennium, I did 2000 Hindu squats to ring in the year 2000. Set squat and pushup goals to motivate yourself and get to work. It is a great feeling of accomplishment to surpass what you now envision as impossible or "crazy."

Ripped Muscles — These exercises are not "bodybuilding" exercises designed to get you "ripped." Yes, you will get stronger and more muscular. Your body will also get leaner. But the primary purpose of these exercises is the development of functional fitness. That means strength, endurance and flexibility. Bodybuilders do not have functional athletic muscles. Their muscles are tight, stiff and cramped and in a combat situation, they are the first to get injured. Bodybuilders don't have much for endurance, either. And surprise, surprise ... in most cases, despite their big showy muscles, they aren't very strong. If you want bodybuilder muscles, study bodybuilding. If you want functional fitness, study ***Combat Conditioning.***

Clothing and Equipment — If you're training in the privacy of your own home, you'll be most comfortable if you exercise with a minimal amount of clothing. Having a mirror before you while you train is a good idea as you can observe your exercise form. Other than that, you don't need anything but a towel and a soft mat for some of the bridging exercises. Although I am wearing shoes in the pictures contained in this book, when I train at home I am in bare feet. Training without shoes strengthens the feet.

n — As your technique in performing the exercises improves, you will get into a rhythm ntimes you'll be so focused that all thoughts of the past and future fade away. This is a ıt is desired while you train, but don't worry if this doesn't happen to you right away. ..cise and upon your breathing and you'll go far.

Focused Breathing — Breathing should be deep and natural, with no impediments. Inhale and exhale with each movement. Keep your mind focused upon your breathing and upon the muscles you are training. By focusing on the muscles you are training, you will get more results than if you let you mind wander.

What Do The Exercises Do For You? The exercises in this book strengthen the muscles of the torso, the abdominals, the lower and upper back, the hips, spine, neck, thighs, arms, hands and feet. The functioning of your internal organs will improve as well and each day you'll notice other physical and psychological benefits.

Weight Loss and Reduced Body Fat — These exercises go a long way in helping to reduce excess weight and body fat. For optimum results, however, do not rely on exercise alone. Follow a natural diet of meats, fruits and vegetables and your job will be that much easier. Avoid white starchy foods. As a general rule, avoid anything that comes in a bag, box or wrapper.

How Long Do I Need To Continue The Program? How long do you need to continue brushing your teeth or taking a shower? Exercise is a daily duty. It is not something to avoid or escape from. Animals in the wild never miss a day of exercise. Take a domesticated dog and lock him up for a week and he'll go stir-crazy. There is something to be learned from this. As Eugen Sandow once said, "Life is movement." Once you stop moving, you're dead. Choose life.

> *Do the thing and you will have the power."*
>
> ***– Emerson***

The Royal Court

The Royal Court in ***Combat Conditioning*** is comprised of the three most important exercises for developing the entire body: Hindu squats, Hindu pushups and bridging.

When I say entire body, though, I am not simply referring to the muscles. I am also talking about the lungs, the heart, the kidneys, the spine and all the internal organs and glands. When you exercise, think of training everything from the inside out. This means that deep and concentrated breathing plays a major role. Training without a concentrated mind is not nearly as beneficial as having a focused mind. Training without deep breathing is a mistake as well. When you train you want to put yourself into another state - a mindset in which the only thing you're thinking about is yourself. Thoughts of the future or the past are not important. Stay in the here and now.

Right from the get-go you should know that a person who does not do Hindu squats is not really doing ***Combat Conditioning.*** Hindu squats lay the foundation for strength and endurance. They build lung power, as well as the thighs, lower back, calves, chest, shoulders and arms. The deep breathing alone will expand the chest and make it larger and more prominent. Additionally, Hindu Squats develop balance, something that is essential to success in combat sports.

Hindu pushups follow the squats. They build strength throughout the torso and arms. The arch involved in this movement stretches and strengthens the spine, hips and shoulders.

As great and important as Hindu squats and pushups are, however, the KING of the ROYAL COURT is the back bridge. It exericises the entire body from head to toe. Many people mistakenly think the back bridge is bad for your neck. The exact opposite is true. Those people who do not have current injuries to the cervical vertebrae, will find the back bridge strengthening the neck, back, thighs, hips and buttocks like nothing else. How can this be done if all the stress is only on the neck? It clearly isn't when done properly.

Many people with neck and back pain feel like new after less than a month of bridging. I can't tell you how many people I know who have been helped by learning the back bridge. All I can say is I've lost count and the number is growing by the day.

If, at the present time, your neck and back are so rigid and inflexible that you cannot do the bridge, begin with the Wall Walking exercise. When your flexibility improves you can start bridging on the floor. Bear in mind, however, that wall walking is another version of the bridge and it can be used even when you already have a good bridge. I practice wall walking regularly as it keeps my spine flexible and helps push my agility to new levels.

Okay, enough of the preliminaries. Let's get you started.

1
2
3
4
5

Hindu Squats

Hindu Squats are the first exercise taught in ***Combat Conditioning.*** They build strength and endurance throughout the thighs, calves, lower back and chest. Most importantly, though, they build lung power. If you can run several miles at a decent clip or pound the Stairmaster for a half hour, you probably think you have good cardiovascular fitness. Great. Now try 500-straight Hindu squats on for size. I think you'll be amazed.

1. Begin with your feet shoulder-width apart and your toes pointing straight ahead. Your hands are pulled in tightly to your chest. Inhale.
2. Keep you back fairly straight and lower your buttocks until your thighs are parallel to the floor.
3. As you lower your buttocks your hands are BEHIND your back, and they follow you toward the ground.
4. As you move toward the parallel-to-the-ground position, you should simultaneously raise your heels from the floor.
5. Now swing your arms upward and push off your toes, raising your body to a standing position.
6. As you raise your body, your hands come IN FRONT of your body. They continue to rise until they are level with your chest.
7. Once you have reached the up-position, you pull your arms in toward your chest again, as if you are rowing a boat. Make tight fists with your hands and pull. Your elbows will be close to your body as you pull.
8. Inhale as you pull your arms in, exhale as you lower yourself.
9. Repeat without stopping for as many reps as possible. In the beginning, depending on your condition, you will be able to do 25-50. When you can do 100 without stopping, you're making great strides.
10. When you can do 500-straight Hindu squats, you're on the way to greatness.

Note: Hindu squats can also be done with your feet flat. On New Year's Eve of the year 2000, I did 2000 Hindu squats to ring in the new millenium. When doing those high numbers, I found it best to alternate between Hindu squats with my heels elevated and Hindu squats with my heels flat. Additionally, I mixed in quite a few Hindu jumper squats, which you will see on pages 28 and 29.

Important Hindu Squat Tips: If you are unable to do Hindu squats without knee pain, either due to previous injuries or an existing problem, you may find it helpful to begin with the Wall Chair exercise as seen on pp. 42-43. You can do the Wall Chair as a simple posture exercise, held for time, while breathing deeply and concentrating. Or you can make it into an isometric exercise. If you do it as an isometric exerice, get into position and press your feet into the ground. Also, firmly press your back against the wall. Press as hard as you can while making the "ssssss" sound. Hold for at least six seconds; longer if you'd like. Just remember to inhale deeply and make an "sssss" as you exhale. Don't forget: It's important that you consult a physician before beginning any fitness program.

1

2

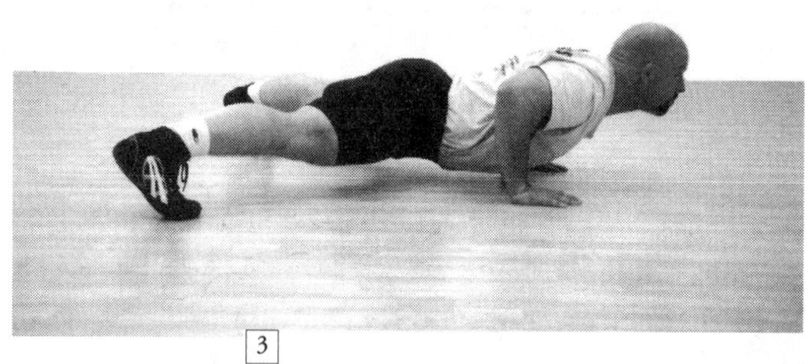

3

4

Hindu Pushups

The Hindu pushup is an exercise, like Hindu squats, that has been used by Indian wrestlers for centuries to build upper body strength and endurance. What makes this exercise so dynamic is that while building strength and stamina, you are also increasing the flexibility of the spine, hips and shoulders. When combined with deep breathing Hindu pushups also build lung power. For those who are used to regular pushups, you'll find these to be quite a challenge. If you can bench press 400 pounds, I'll bet dollars to donuts that you'll struggle with 25-straight Hindu pushups.

1. Start with your hands on the floor, shoulder-width apart.
2. Your feet are on the floor (no knees) and your legs are shoulder width or wider, depending on your flexibility.
3. Starting position is butt in the air, head looking back to your heels.
4. Bend your elbows and lower your body in a circular arc, until your arms are straight. Your chest is up and your hips are almost touching the ground.
5. Look to the ceiling. Inhale.
6. Push back toward your heels once again. Straightening your arms and stretching your legs, as in step #3. Exhale.
7. Back to the same position as described in step #4.
8. Do as many repetitions as you can.

Important Hindu Pushup Tips:

1. If you experience shoulder pain while doing Hindu pushups or if you are not able to do them due to a previous injury, I have a suggestion. It may be far better for you to hold off on the Hindu pushups while you concentrate on strengthening your shoulders from every direction and angle with the rubber chest expanders put out by Lifeline USA. Once you have balanced strength in your shoulders from using the chest expanders, you may find that you can do Hindu pushups without any pain at all. For information on the chest expanders go to mattfurey.com/expander.html. Also, remember to consult your physician before engaging in any exercise program.
2. Some people lack the strength to do a single Hindu pushup when they begin. If you fall into this category, not to worry. Start with an isometric Hindu pushup. Get into the start position and press your hands into the ground as hard as you can. Hold for six seconds while you make the "sssss" sound. After this move into the arched position. While looking skyward, flex and contract your body and push your hands into the ground. Hold for six seconds while making the "sssss" sound. Repeat this entire sequence three times. These isometric presses will give you strength very quickly and soon you'll be doing a full Hindu pushup.

Back Bridge

The back bridge is the greatest exercise in the entire ***Combat Conditioning*** repertoire. It is the KING. Most people think the back bridge only works your neck, but it does far more than that. In addition to promoting flexibility in your spine, the back bridge builds the muscles in your abdominals, legs, hips, buttocks, back, shoulders and neck. That's quite a load, wouldn't you say?

The back bridge is one of the most misunderstood training movements in existence.Before looking at the pictures and instructions on how to do a proper back bridge, it is important to lay some ground work on the subject.

One of the things you'll find written in some books is a panic-like warning about bridging. These books tell you that it is dangerous, that you shouldn't do it, that, in fact, you shouldn't do any neck exercises with a weight that is greater than your own head. One of the common themes is that bridging "compresses the cervical vertebrae of the spine."

The exact opposite is true. Bridging stretches the spine and the muscles along the spine, everything from the coccyx through the cervical vertebrae. Take one of those skeletons doctors have in their offices and lean the head back and tell me if the cervical vertebrae are compressed. Then go to a chiropractor to get your spine adjusted. How does he do it? He doesn't jar you up, does he? No, he stretches you out.

A simpler example is as follows: If you pull on a bow string is it compressed or stretched? It is stretched.

How people have come to believe that stretching the neck and spine with bridging is compression is beyond me.

Combat athletes who dismiss bridging as a dangerous exercise have either never done it, can't do it (either because of fear or a preexisting neck injury), are simply repeating without first-hand knowledge what someone else told them ... or they are just plain dumb.

There is no exercise that will strengthen your neck as much as proper bridging. The key, however, is in knowing how to do it. Unfortunately, most people never learn the proper method. Most bridge on the top of the head.

This is the way I was taught to do it as well, but it is wrong. The proper method of doing a back bridge requires you to place all the weight on your forehead, not on the top of your head. You must arch your entire spine. Your hips and abdominals must thrust forward and your chest should be expanded as well. And from this position you continue to arch, relaxing your shoulder and neck muscles until your nose touches the mat.

This may seem like an impossibility, and it may be for those who are sick, frail, weak, afraid or injured. But it isn't for most people. In fact, over the last couple months I have taught many people, young and not so young, how to do the bridge, and some of them were able to touch their noses on the first try. Others were not able to do so right away, but after a month or two of steadfast practice, were able to nail it.

Your sole focus, however, is not simply getting your nose to the mat. Once you have attained the perfect bridge (forehead and nose on the mat with feet flat on the floor and arms folded across chest), you are to hold this position for three minutes. Count silently to 200 and you've done it. Believe me, holding a perfect bridge for three minutes is no easy task, and once you can do it you're really doing well.

The above represents how you get started on the path to building a powerful neck. No other neck exercise can give you the results that bridging will. Neck isometrics don't do it. Lying on a bench with a plate resting on your head doesn't do it. Neck harnesses don't do it and neck machines should be avoided at all costs as they bind, cramp and put kinks in the muscles of the neck.

Do you know why the other exercises don't work as well as bridging? It's because all the other exercises isolate the neck muscles. Proper bridging does NOT isolate the neck muscles. It works the muscles along your entire spine as well as the buttocks, hips and thighs. In short, bridging is a movement that involves most of your body.

Important Bridging Tips:

If the bridging exercises seem next to impossible, you may want to begin with light bridging on a stability ball. Get one of these balls and lie on it so that you're looking at the ceiling. Then gently reach your hands backward and slowly arch your spine. Pay attention to your breathing and simply "RELAX." Allow your spine and the muscles of your back to loosen. Once you find a comfortable position that is a good stretch, just hold it and breathe naturally. This will help you ease into the other bridges. Or you can simply stick with the bridge on the ball. Again, be sure to consult a physician before beginning any fitness program.

Bridge With Hand Support

1. Lie down on a soft mat with your back facing down.
2. Bend your legs and place the palms of your hands by your shoulders.
3. Drive off your legs and push off your hands until you are placing weight on the top of your head.
4. Once you are on the top of your head, arch your lower back and push your chest forward. Strive to touch your nose to the mat behind you.
5. Rock back and forth, trying to go further each time. Take your time though. If you don't have the flexibility just yet, be patient. Eventually it'll come. Don't force it.
6. Go back and forth 10-20 times.
7. Inhale when you push upward. Exhale when you come down.

The mind can be very powerful. Using mine to its fullest has always been my number one priority as I worked to improve my racing career. Your mind, however is no different than your physical body – you need to condition it.

– Bobby Unser
3 x Indianapolis 500 winner

Bridge With Arms Folded Across Chest, Heels Up

Once you are able to touch your nose to the mat, you're ready to progress to the following variation.

1. Lie down on a soft mat with your back facing down.
2. Bend your legs and place the palms of your hands by your shoulders.
3. Drive off your legs and push off your hands until you are placing weight on the top of your head.
4. Once you are on the top of your head, arch your lower back and push your chest forward. Strive to touch your nose to the mat behind you.
5. Once you have touched your nose to the mat, stay there and fold your arms across your chest.
6. Now rock back and forth, trying to go further each time.
7. Go back and forth 10-20 times.
8. Inhale when you push upward. Exhale when you come down.

Never be afraid to lose "friends." A true friend is someone who takes pride in seeing you succeed. Some friends can only handle your success to a certain point - then they get jealous. If and when that happens, slice them out of your life immediately and never look back. When one door closes another opens.

And take it from someone who knows: The new door is much bigger, much broader and brings much more success and happiness your way.

– from Matt Furey's daily email tips - free at MattFurey.com

Bridge With Arms Folded Across Chest, Heels Flat

Once you are able to touch your nose with arms folded across your chest and heels off the ground, work on doing the next variation.

1. Lie down on a soft mat with your back facing down.
2. Bend your legs and place the palms of your hands by your shoulders.
3. Drive off your legs and push off your hands until you are placing weight on the top of your head.
4. Once you are on the top of your head, arch your lower back and push your chest forward. Strive to touch your nose to the mat behind you.
5. Once you have touched your nose to the mat, stay there and fold your arms across your chest.
6. Now lower your heels to the mat and keep your back arched so that your nose is still touching the mat.
7. Breathe naturally and hold this position for as long as you can. Relax and concentrate on your breathing. Shoot for three minutes and count your breathes. When you can hold for three minutes, while taking fewer than 20 breathes, you're making tremendous progress. My personal record is 8 breathes in three minutes.

Note: After doing this exercise, it is a good idea to stretch the other way by doing the front bridge, located in the supplementary exercises section that follows.

Important: Although the bridge has helped eliminate chronic neck and back pain for many people, it is not for everyone. Please consult your physician before performing this bridge or any other bridge in this book

> *Pursue one great decisive aim with force and determination.*
>
> ***– Major General Karl von Clausewitz***

Important: Come to my website at **www.MattFurey.com** and give me your name and e-mail address. In return I promise to send you a free fitness tip every single day. My tips will keep you focused, informed and inspired. And they will entertain you beyond belief. For an example of the kind of material I will send you, check out pages 30 and 134 in this book. ***M.F.***

Supplementary Exercises

After working on the exercises in the ROYAL COURT for one month, you can begin adding one or more of the supplementary exercises that follow. Go as you like, but stick with the foundation.

Some of the following exercises are easy and others are pretty darn difficult. Choose those that you think will benefit you the most. Do not however, jump into the most difficult exercises before you are ready.

The supplementary exercises add variety and keep your enthusiasm for training in high gear.

Hindu Jumper Squats

Jumper squats are great to do by themselves or in combination with regular Hindu squats. You'll find yourself huffing and puffing in no time and you know what that means. LUNG POWER! Begin this exercise from the same position as the Hindu squats.

1. Jump forward six inches landing in a squat with your heels elevated.
2. Make sure that both feet touch the ground simultaneously.
3. As you jump forward, inhale as your arms go behind your back.
4. Jump back to the starting point and exhale as your arms swing upward and pull backward.
5. Repeat this movement over and over until fatigued. Shoot for 10- 20 repetitions at first. Eventually you'll be able to do 100 repetitions or more. This exercise will get you huffing and puffing and will burn fat like nobody's business.

Important: Come to my website at **www.MattFurey.com** and give me your name and e-mail address. In return I promise to send you a free fitness tip every single day. My tips will keep you focused, informed and inspired. And they will entertain you beyond belief. For an example of the kind of material I will send you, check out pages 30 and 134 in this book. ***M.F.***

One Leg in Air Pushups

These pushups are about as close you can get to doing a one-arm pushup while using the other arm for balance. It really works the shoulders and arms.

1. Start with your hands on the floor, shoulder-width apart.
2. Your feet are together.
3. Starting position is like that of a regular pushup.
4. Lift your left leg in the air and turn the right side of your body downward as you lower your right side toward the floor.
5. Now push yourself back up.
6. Now lift your right leg in the air and repeat with the left arm.
7. Inhale as you lower yourself. Exhale as you come back to the starting position.
8. Do as many repetitions as you can.

> *Talent is useless without training, thank God.*
>
> ***– Mark Twain***

Wall Walking

This exercise is another one that stretches and strengthens all the muscles along the spine. It also works the abdominals as they involuntarily contract when you bend backwards. Increased flexibility and strength in the spine goes a long way toward increasing energy levels and improving overall health.

1. Stand with your back and heels flat against the wall.
2. Take two steps, heel to toe, until you are three feet from the wall.
3. From there, lean backward with your hands stretched above your head.
4. Slowly move your hands down the wall. Continue walking until the top of your head lightly touches the floor.
5. Turn to your stomach and stand up again.
6. Do five to ten repetitions.
7. Breathe naturally.

What counts is not necessarily the size of the dog in the fight –
it's the size of the fight in the dog.

General Dwight David Eisenhower

Wall Walking to Back Bridge to Chest on Wall

This exercise begins like Wall Walking, but once you reach the floor, you're going to go into a back bridge. Do this exercise slowly.

1. Stand with your back and heels flat against the wall.
2. Take two steps, heel to toe, until you are three steps from the wall.
3. From there, lean backward with your hands stretched above your head.
4. Slowly move your hands down the wall. Continue walking until the top of your head touches the floor.
5. Now put your palms flat on the floor and arch your spine.
6. Slowly push up and back, trying to touch your chest to the wall behind you.
7. If you cannot touch it, slowly rock back and forth and keep trying.
8. Once you are able to touch, hold for 10 to 30 seconds while breathing naturally.
9. Now rock back and forth, touching your chest to the wall 5-10 more times.

Note: After doing this exercise, be sure to stand and bend forward from the waist to stretch your spine in the other direction.

> *Pec deck, cable crossovers, triceps kickbacks… all those overly isolationist, pretty-boy movements are not only pointless, but you're going to injure yourself, because you end up building your body in a way that isn't functional. It's a good idea to think of the body as one unit, not a bunch of unconnected muscles.*
>
> ***– from a Matt Furey interview***

Wall Walking With Reverse Pushup

This exercise begins like Wall Walking, but once you reach the floor, you're going to get an upper body workout like you won't believe (especially your shoulders).

1. Stand with your back and heels flat against the wall.
2. Take two steps, heel to toe, until you are three steps from the wall.
3. From there, lean backward with your hands stretched above your head.
4. Slowly move your hands down the wall. Continue walking until the top of your head touches the floor.
5. Now put your palms flat on the floor.
6. Do a reverse pushup.
7. Hold this position, then walk back up the wall.
8. Breathe naturally as you do this exercise.
9. Do five to ten repetitions.

> *Anyone can "start," but only the thouroughbred will "finish!"*
>
> ***– Napoleon Hill***

Wall Chair

This exercise is another great one for building strength in the legs. It is used to torture wrestlers at the end of a hard workout, but skiers use it as well. When doing this exercise, pay attention to your breathing. Keep your attention focused on a single point and hold as long as you can.

1. Place your back against a wall and sit like a chair with your feet shoulder-width apart.
2. Fold your arms across your chest.
3. Look straight ahead.
4. Relax and breathe deeply.
5. Hold for one minute.

As you progress in this exercise you will be able to hold it for longer periods of time.

Tell the world what you're going to do, but show them first.

– from Matt Furey's daily email tips - free at MattFurey.com

Stationary Hand Stand

Holding a hand stand is much harder than it looks. It builds tremendous upper body strength, especially in the shoulders. This exercise is also great for increasing blood flow to the brain.

1. Place your palms flat on the floor, about a foot from the wall.
3. Kick one leg up, then the other, until you are holding a hand stand.
4. Stay in this position for as long as you can.
5. Breathe naturally and focus on the muscles in your shoulders and arms.
6. Come down slowly.

> *An aim in life is the only fortune worth finding; and it is not to be found in foreign lands, but in the heart itself.*
>
> ***– Robert Lewis Stevenson***

Front Bridge

After holding the back bridge and working on it for awhile, you'll want to spend some time in the front bridge to even things out.

1. Rest the top of your head on a soft mat. Your knees are off the ground and your hands are behind your back.
2. Tuck your chin until it touches the upper part of your chest.
3. Keep your feet flat on the floor, legs straight.
4. Breathe naturally and hold this position.
5. Go easy at first, but keep time. Eventually you'll want to be able to hold this bridge for three minutes.

Everything you want to do or become, begins first in your imagi-nation. It truly is the strongest nation on earth.

– from Matt Furey's daily email tips - free at MattFurey.com

Body-by-Fury

Whirling Dervish

This exercise is a popular one in Iran and other Middle-Eastern countries where wrestling is the national sport. It is also an exercise recommended by Tibetan monks for increasing one's life span and for bringing all organs and energy centers of the body into a improved state of health. It increases energy and endurance and greatly improves your balance.

1. From a standing position, place your arms shoulder-high and stretch them outward with the palms facing down.
2. Pick a spot in front of yourself to focus on.
3. Pivot your feet slowly and spin your body clockwise. If you feel comfortable with this exercise, gradually add speed.
4. Do 10 to 25 repetitions, then stop and wait until the room stops spinning.
5. You can then spin counterclockwise if you'd like, but it isn't necessary.
6. Breathe naturally while performing this exercise.

It's one thing to push and pull a weight around, it's quite another to master your own bodyweight from every conceivable angle and direction.

– from a Matt Furey interview

Reverse Pushups

The reverse pushup is one of the best overall exercises you can do. It not only strengthens your back, shoulders and arms, but it promotes flexibility and suppleness throughout your entire upper body, especially the shoulders and spine.

1. Starting from your back with your knees bent and feet flat on the floor, place your hands next to the tops of your shoulders with your palms on the ground.
2. Push your body off the floor until your arms reach the locked position. The crown of your head should be facing the floor.
3. Push yourself forward. Make your body into a wheel by trying to get your chest even with your hands.
4. Slowly lower yourself, bringing your upper back and neck to the floor.
5. Do as many repetitions as possible.
6. Exhale at the top of the movement, inhale at the bottom.

Leg Lifts Behind Head

Leg lifts done in this manner are great for strengthening the abdominals, lower back and hip flexors. Each time you bring your feet behind your head, you are also stretching the spine, shoulders and upper back. This movement is also great for its effect upon the internal organs. All abdominal exercises help aid the body in the digestion and eliminative process.

1. Lie on your back with your hands at your sides.
2. Lift your head until your chin is almost touching your chest.
3. Hold your head up while you lift your legs in the air.
4. Focus your attention on your abdominals.
5. Continue raising your legs until your toes touch behind your head.
6. Lower your legs back to the ground, letting them softly touch the floor.
7. Inhale up, exhale down.
8. Do as many repetitions as you can.

> *Every failure is a blessing in disguise, providing it teaches some needed lesson one could not have learned without it.*
>
> ***– Napoleon Hill***

Fingertip Pushups

Fingertip pushups are great for developing the strength in your fingers and hands while also developing the chest, shoulders and arms. Once you get good at doing them on all your fingers, you increase resistance by reducing the number of fingers you use. When you can do a one-finger pushup, it'll be time for you to write a book on conditioning as well.

1. Start with your hands on the floor, shoulder-width apart.
2. Your feet are together.
3. Put all the weight of your upper body on the fingertips of both hands.
4. Lower your chest until you can touch the floor with it.
5. Push yourself back up.
6. Do as many repetitions as you can.
7. Inhale as you lower yourself. Exhale as you come back to the starting position.

Matt,

I noticed in one of your recent e-mails that you said bench pressing wasn't healthy.
I was wondering why push ups are healthy yet bench pressing isn't – does it have to do with the fact that in a push up your whole body helps in support?
P.S. I'm not doing any bench pressing, only the exercises in ***Combat Conditioning****.*

Brandon L. Marzolf

M.F.: *Brandon, most people who do the bench press set a goal to pile on as much weight as possible so they can set a personal record. This is natural and normal – but in order to increase their bench press total – many people end up destroying their rotator cuff. This is increasingly common today because the BENCH is what people look to for a measure of their strength. They think big pecs are the source of your power. They're not. When doing a pushup, the shoulder joint is not supporting excessive weight, nor is it put into an unnatural or compromised position. So pushups are far better for you from a health and fitness stand point than the bench press. And with all the variations of them you can do, including handstand, one-arm and so on – you'll get far more FUNCTIONAL strength from pushups than you ever will from benching.*

– from Matt Furey's daily email tips - free at MattFurey.com

Kneeling Back Bend

This exercise is tremendous for increasing flexibility and strength throughout your back and thighs. Your hip flexors and buttocks are strengthened as well. Additionally, in all back bend movements your abdominals get a great workout because they are contracted in order to help stabilize you. You can literally get all the abdominal training you need from an exercise like this.

1. Kneel on the floor with your palms resting on the back of your thighs.
2. Keep your back straight and your hips forward.
3. Let you head fall backward and gradually lower yourself toward the floor.
4. Go only as far as your body will allow. Do not force this movement.
5. Once you have reached the limit of your flexibility, return to the starting position.
6. As you return to the starting position, keep your back straight and your hips forward.
7. Inhale down, exhale up.
8. Shoot for 10 – 25 repetitions.

> *If people knew how hard I worked to acquire my mastery, they wouldn't think it worthwhile at all.*
>
> ***– Michaelangelo***

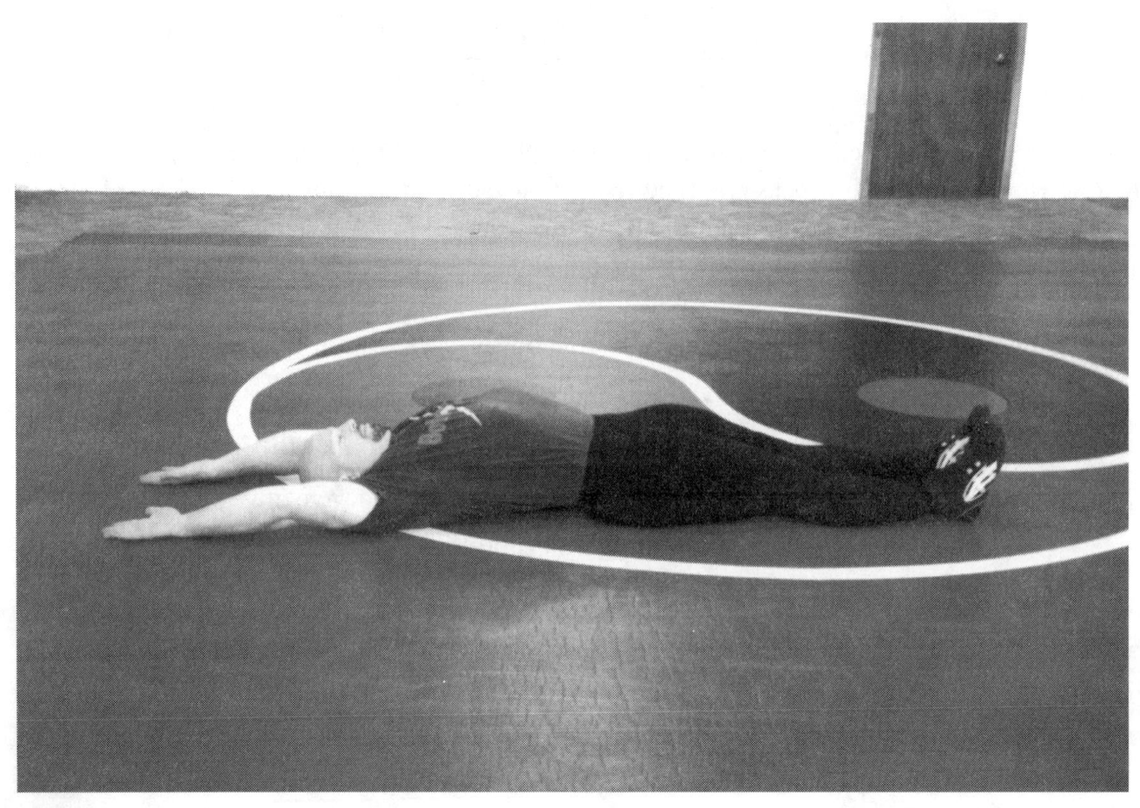

V-ups

V-ups are great for exercising the upper and lower abdominals at the same time. They also train you in agility. Once again, the internal organs are massaged by this exercise, aiding in the digestion and eliminative process.

1. Lie down on your back with your legs straight and arms extended above your head.
2. Simultaneously raise your arms and legs in the air above your mid-section.
3. Touch your hands to your feet.
4. Lower your arms and legs back to the floor. Do not let your feet touch the ground.
5. Repeat until you cannot do anymore repetitions.
6. Inhale up, exhale down.

NOTE: If you feel pain in your neck or lower back when doing this exercise, it means you are weak in those areas. Do not run out to the local fitness equipment store and invest in an abdominal gadget that allows you to rest the back of your head on a cushion. If a muscle is weak, you don't ignore it or give it a rest - you train it.

For those of you with severe neck or back pain, see a physician who isn't out on the golf course, or a chiropractor who will give you more than two minutes of his time.

Table Maker

This exercise is great for increasing strength in the upper and lower back, triceps, shoulders, hip and buttocks. It also promotes greater flexibility in the spine.

1. Sit on the floor with your legs straight and your hands palm down at your sides.
2. Push your body forward until the soles of your feet are flat on the ground. At the same time arch your hips and back and let your head fall backward.
3. Squeeze your buttocks tightly and push the soles of your feet into the ground.
4. Straighten your back as much as you can.
5. Hold this position for a count or so, then return to the floor.
6. Do 10-20 repetitions of this exercise.
7. Inhale up, exhale down.

You are today where your thoughts have brought you. You will be tomorrow where your thoughts take you.

– James Allen

The Stretcher

This exercise is a variation of the Tablemaker. It is also great for increasing strength in the upper and lower back, triceps, shoulders, hip and buttocks. It is more difficult than the Tablemaker and promotes greater strength and flexibility in the lower back and hips.

1. Sit on the floor with your legs straight and your hands palm down at your sides.
2. Push your body forward until the soles of your feet are flat on the ground and your legs are straight. At the same time arch your hips and back and let your head fall backward.
3. Squeeze your buttocks tightly and push the soles of your feet into the ground.
4. Straighten your back as much as you can.
5. Hold this position for a count or so, then return to the floor.
6. Do 10-20 repetitions of this exercise.
7. Inhale up, exhale down.

A Sample From the Matt Furey Inner Circle @ www.MattFureyInnerCircle.com

For Some People, Isometrics Are The Way to Start

Depending upon how much time a person has been sedentary and what his/her physical condition is at the moment, isometric holds of ***Combat Conditioning*** *exercises are a great place to begin. Why? Because the person doesn't have the strength or the coordination to do the full movement just yet. For example, some people cannot do a single Hindu pushup – or a single regular pushup when they begin training. This can be discouraging, but it need not be. If this person simply holds the pushup position in the "up" position and presses into the ground as hard as possible, he will build tremendous strength. Key thing is to press hard for six seconds while making the "sssss" sound. The same can be done from the beginning and finishing positions of the Hindu pushup, with the wall chair, with the v-up or jack-knife situp, and so on. – Now, for the real kicker that may surprise you: These and other types of isometrics that I'll be teaching very soon, will also greatly advance the person who is great at doing bodyweight calisthenics… even the people who are doing big numbers. – I remember teaching some of them to Ed Baran, "Master of Handstands" – when I was in China last November. The next day when we spoke by phone, I said, "So what do you think about those isometrics I told you to do?" Ed's answer: "I'm embarrassed to say, but they kicked my ass." Moral of the story: Isometrics are great for the person who cannot physically do full repetitions of squats, pushups, pullups and the like. They are also good for those who can.*

– More to come. - M.F.

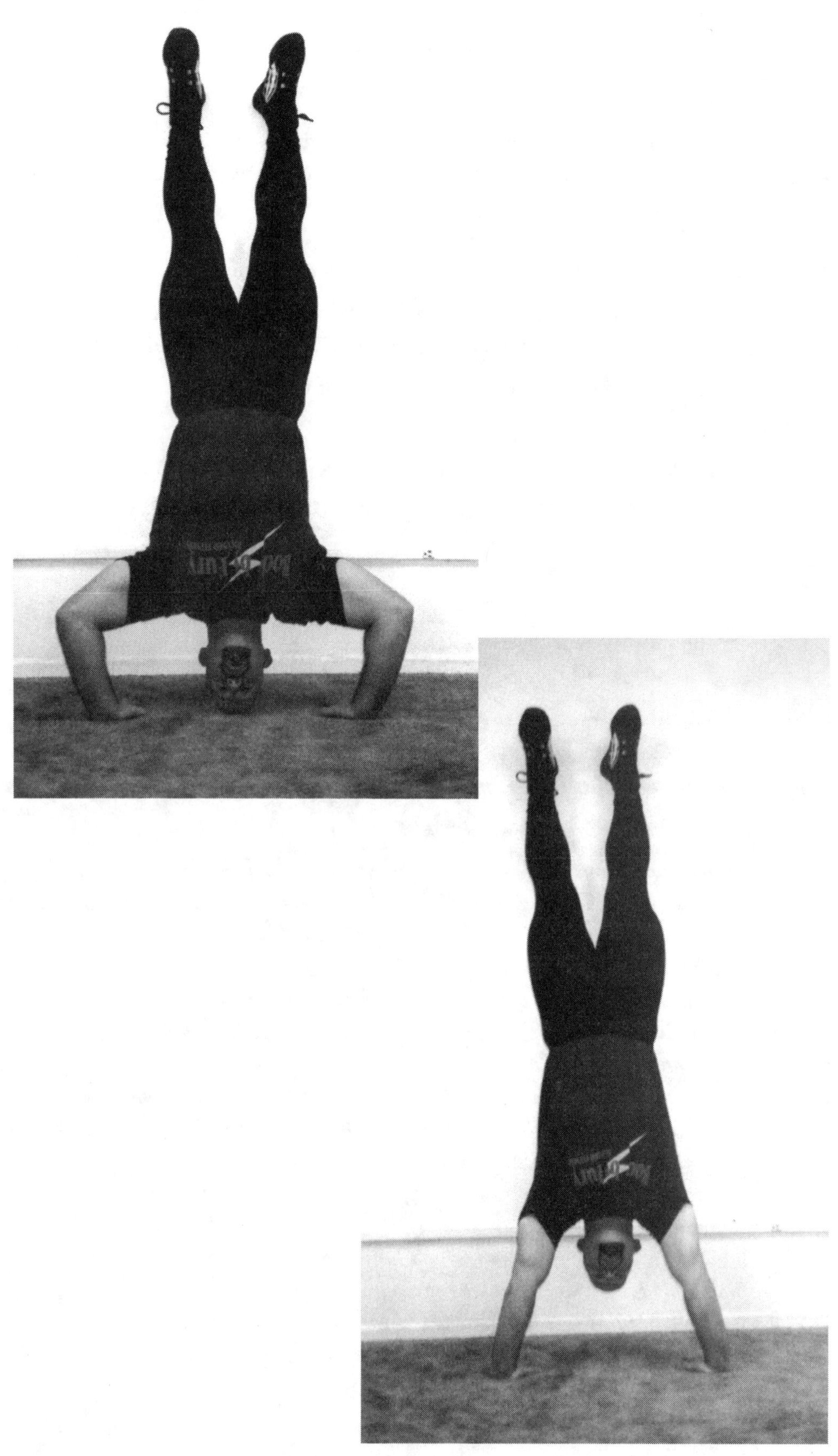

Handstand Pushups

The handstand pushup is an exercise that builds shoulder, back and arm strength. Anyone who wants to get a lot stronger should do a lot of these. When you are doing this exercise with ease, you're getting an idea of what it is like to handle your own bodyweight from all directions and angles.

1. Put your hands on the floor, about shoulder-width apart.
2. Making sure no windows are in front or behind you, kick up until your legs are balanced along the wall. Your knees are bent and your weight is resting on your palms. Your back is now to the wall.
3. From this position, lower yourself until your head touches the floor, then push straight up and lock out your arms. Exhale.
4. Do as many as you can, which at first, may be a big fat ZERO. If you can't do one yet, make it an isometric movement and push and push and push until your muscles have had enough.
5. When you can do 10-straight repetitions you're making good progress.

In ***The Secret Power of Handstand Training***, Ed Baran and I, teach you 21 different ways to train your handstand pushups. For more information, go to www.mattfurey.com/handstand_training.html

Side Bends

Side bends are great for strengthening the side of your waist (obliques). Part of ***Combat Conditioning*** is gaining flexibility and strength in all directions; sideways is no exception.

1. Stand with your feet shoulder-width apart.
2. Raise your left arm in the air so that the biceps is almost touching your ear.
3. Bend to your right as far as you can. Once you have reached the extreme stretch of this movement, then move back and forth a couple inches, repeating the final phase of the movement 50-100 times.
4. Switch sides and repeat.
5. Breathe naturally throughout this movement.

> *The joy is in creating, not maintaining.*
>
> ***– Vince Lombardi***

Jumping Lunges

Like Hindu squats, jumping lunges build explosive strength and muscular endurance in the lower body and a ton of lung power as well. Whenever you think your workout is getting too easy, add some jumping lunges and you'll quickly change your mind.

1. Stand with your feet shoulder-width apart. Hands on hips.
2. Jump forward and lunge downward with your left leg. Make sure your knee doesn't touch the floor. Jump back to the starting position.
3. Switch legs and repeat the same movement.
4. Repeat this movement over and over, adding speed whenever possible.
5. Inhale down, exhale up.
6. Do as many repetitions as possible.

Concentration is the secret of strength in politics, in war, in trade, in short in all management of human affairs.

– Emerson

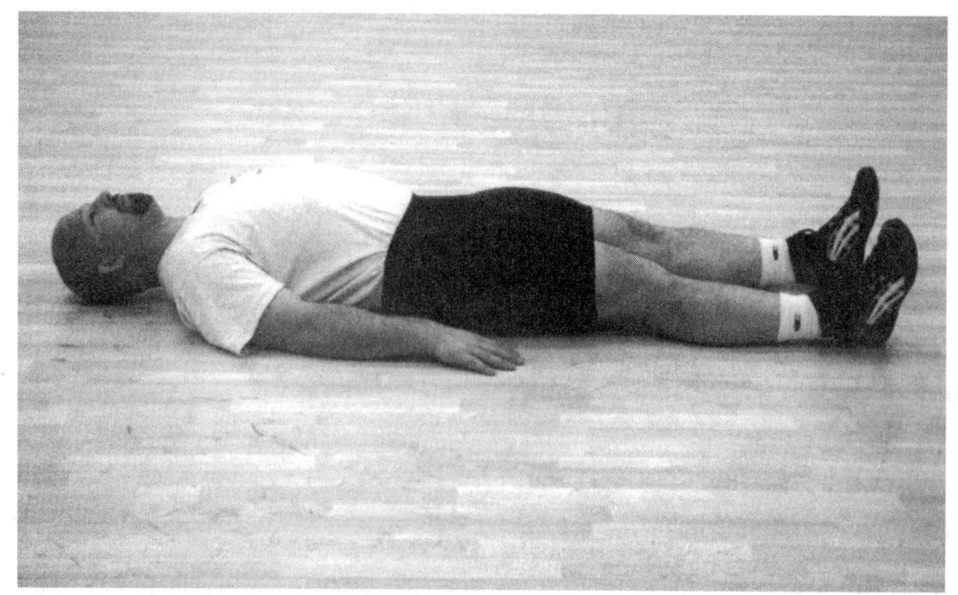

No Momentum Sit-ups

One of the reasons why I like doing sit-ups this way is because you can't pull on your head or neck to cheat yourself up. Also, when done this way you literally feel how much momentum you used to use to do a sit-up. This method gives you a real test for the strength of your midsection. It strengthens the abdominals, lower back and hip flexors.

1. Lie on the floor with straight legs. Your hands are at your side, palms flat.
2. Without letting your heels or legs to come off the floor, use your abdominal muscles to sit up.
3. Come all the way up until your torso is perpendicular to the floor.
4. Return to start and repeat as many times as possible.
5. Inhale up, exhale down.

*There truly is nothing like shifting your metabolism into overdrive. Hill sprints and the other exercises in **Combat Conditioning** really do the trick. The key is choosing compound movements that hit the largest muscle groups – and the more you hit at the same time, the better.*

– from Matt Furey's daily email tips - free at MattFurey.com

Bowing

This exercise comes from the oldest style of kung fu known to man. It happens to be a grappling art, and this movement will get you huffing and puffing in a hurry, as it requires full body explosiveness. It is much more than bowing; it is more like using a sledge hammer.

1. Stand with feet about shoulder-width apart.
2. Bend your knees and lower your buttocks to a position just above the wall chair position.
3. Make fists with your hands and place them above your head. One hand is above the other.
4. Focus on your abdominals. Imagine you have a sledge hammer in your hands and you're going to drive it into the concrete.
5. Throw your hands forward and downward while straightening your legs and sliding backwards on the soles of your feet.
6. Exhale down, inhale up.
7. Do 10-20 repetitions.

Determine that the thing can and shall be done, and then we shall find a way.

– Abraham Lincoln

Bowing With Partner

Here's another good way to practice lifting another human being. It works your abdominals, lower back and legs.

1. Turn your back to your partner.
2. Allow him to drape his right arm over your shoulder.
3. Grab hold of his wrist with your left hand, then grab his shoulder with your right.
4. With a straight back and slightly bent knees, bow forward from the midsection while straightening your legs.
5. As you bow, focus on making your abdominals do the work.
6. Really pull and feel your abdominal muscles contract. Raise and lower your opponent ten times on each side.
7. Inhale at the bottom of the lift, exhale at the top.

> *Early to bed early to rise, makes a man healthy, wealthy and wise.*
>
> ***– Benjamin Franklin***

Body by Fury
FOCUSED FITNESS

Pushing

This exercise also comes from Shuai-chiao, the oldest style of kung fu known to man. It is similar to jumping jacks, but done with arms pushed out to the front rather than swung overhead. It is great for developing lung power as well as strengthening the legs and upper body.

1. Stand with feet together and fists pulled back to your hips.
2. Jump into the squat position while your palms come straight out and push forward.
3. Now jump back to the starting position with your fists at your hips again.
4. Inhale when you jump out, exhale when you return.
5. Do 50 or more repetitions of this exercise.

*Mother in labor gets a major contraction. She wants it to stop. But whoever is gathered around to assist is making sure she doesn't. Her willingness to endure the pain, to go with the pain, brings forth the new baby. I think there's a lesson in this for all of us, **MEN** included.*

– from Matt Furey's daily email tips - free at MattFurey.com

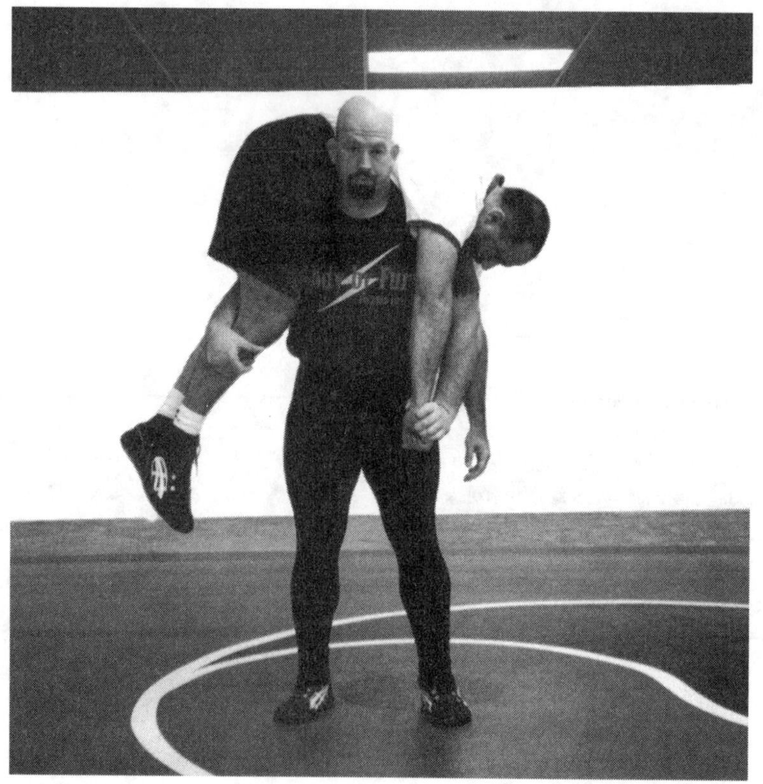

Fireman's Carry With Partner

When you work on lifting the weight of another human being, you'll quickly discover how confined you are with weight training exercises. And talk about functional strength! This is a movement that is used to save people's lives. It develops full body strength and gets you breathing hard mighty fast.

1. Grab your partner by the wrist or by the back of the elbow.
2. Squat beneath him and pull his arm over your shoulder. Your head is between his arm and upper back.
3. From this position, push upward while pulling vigorously on his arm.
4. Keep your back straight.
5. Lower and repeat ten times on each side.
6. Exhale at the top of the lift, inhale at the bottom.

Imagination is the elixir of life.

– P.T. Barnum

Grass Hoppers

This exercise is a great for developing lung power while conditioning your abdominals, hips and thighs. One minute of this will get your attention.

1. Beginning position is on all fours.
2. While keeping your hands on the floor, slightly lift your right leg and slide it under your chest until it touches by your left hand.
3. Without missing a beat, reverse directions and slide your left leg over to your right hand.
4. Do 25-100 repetitions of this exercise.
5. Breathe naturally.

When I was a freshman in high school I was not by any means the MOST talented athlete on the wrestling squad. There were several people who were better than me. But guess what? None of them had the drive that I had because none of them took the time to formulate specific goals they wanted to attain. That's where our differences began – but it is not where they ended.

– from a Matt Furey article

Mountain Climbers

This is the only time you'll "climb a mountain" on all fours, and like grasshoppers, this exercise is great for developing lung power and stamina. It works the thighs, buttocks, hips and abdominals.

1. Beginning position is on all fours.
2. While keeping your hands on the floor, lift your right foot and run straight forward with it until your knee is well under your chest.
3. Without missing a beat, reverse legs. Continue on without stopping.
4. Do 25-100 repetitions of this exercise.
5. Breathe naturally.

> *You will become as small as your controlling desire, as great as your dominant aspiration.*
>
> ***– James Allen***

Duck Waddle

Eric Heiden, a speed skater who won five gold medals in the 1980 Winter Olympics, was a big believer in this exercise. It builds strength throughout the thighs and hips.

1. Assume the squatting position with your hands behind your back.
2. Step forward with your left foot, then your right.
3. Keep walking in this manner until fatigued.
4. Breathe naturally.

To add resistance you can do this exercise up hill.

> *He who is not courageous enough to take risks will accomplish nothing in life.*
>
> ***– Muhammad Ali***

Bear Crawling

Bear crawling is an amazing exercise that develops strength and mobility throughout all the limbs. At the same time, you cannot do this exercise without getting out of breath. This makes it a great developer of lung power.

1. Find a place with a lot of room, be it a field of grass or a large padded room.
2. Place all your weight on the palms of your hands and the soles of your feet.
3. Now step forward with your hands and feet and run like a bear.
4. Breathe naturally as you run.
5. Continue until fatigued.
6. Rest and repeat.

Back in the 1980's, when I was working wrestling camps and clinics around the country for the University of Iowa, we literally put these kids through three and four workouts every single day, for 14-28 days. It really was like bootcamp for these kids.

Anyway, in the afternoon – when I would have the kids do sprints – there were always a number of boys who didn't quite understand English whenever I said "sprint."

These boys would inevitably "dog it" when it came time to run at full speed. So I developed a solution to this problem. Whenever it happened I would stop the entire group and say: "Listen, if you don't want to sprint when I say sprint, no problem. I don't mind. I'll just switch you guys to bear crawls. And when you do the bear crawls, you're 100 percent welcome to go as slow as you want – although you might find that more painful than going fast. The choice is yours.

Well, as the kids weren't exactly sure whether "Sgt. Furey" – as they used to call me, meant biz or not – they tested me.

My reaction to their "test" was immediate. "Okay boys, let's get down on all fours and do the bear crawl."

What was the result? I'll tell you. After two bear crawl sprints – these boys were eager to go back to the bipedal position. And do you know why? Because bear crawls work practically every muscle in your body. They are far superior to running when building endurance, strength and agility. They will have you huffing and puffing in no time flat.

– from Matt Furey's daily email tips - free at MattFurey.com

Crab Walking

Like bear crawling, crab walking is one of the best exercises you can do for overall body conditioning. It works all the limbs and develops lung power. Because you are upside down while doing this exercise, it also works the hips, spine and back a great deal.

1. Find a place with a lot of room, be it a field of grass or a large padded room.
2. Sit on your butt, then place all your weight on the palms of your hands and the soles of your feet.
3. Elevate your body so that only your hands and feet touch the ground. Now move forward with your hands and feet.
4. Breathe naturally as you move.
5. Continue until fatigued.
6. Rest and repeat.

A Sample From the Matt Furey Inner Circle @ www.MattFureyInnerCircle.com

Crab Walks – What Are They Good For?

Want to know what crab walks are good for? The answer is NOT… absolutely nuthin. They're good for your triceps and shoulders. They're good for your legs and hips. They're good for your abs. But the one thing you may not be aware of is that they are great for your… back. That's right. If you have lower back pain – or if you have a weakness in the lower back – believe me, it will be hard keeping your butt off the ground. It will be hard moving while keeping your butt up. But let me tell you, after a few sessions of crab walks, your lower back and everything throughout your "core" will be stronger and more stable. I recommend you either alternate bear crawls with crab walks – or do all your bear crawls, then do crab walks. One week ago my son Frank could barely get his butt off the ground. He whined and cried about how he couldn't "do it." I prodded him on. Yesterday they were a snap for him. Much easier than he figured and now he likes doing them. Tomorrow, another "animal" movement that is great for the lower back.

Stay tuned. – M.F.

Reverse Handstand

The reverse handstand is an exercise that builds a lot of strength in the shoulders, back and arms. In this exercise you simply hold the position for as long as you can. When you can hold for three minutes, you're doing great.

1. Stand with your back to the wall. Bend forward and place your hands on the floor, about shoulder-width apart.
2. Now place the soles of your feet on the wall and walk up it backwards until your chest is flat against the wall.
3. From this position, simply breathe naturally and hold for as long as you can.

Note: It wouldn't be a bad idea to have someone spot you on this exercise at first. It looks much easier than it is.

> *More gold has been mined from the thoughts of men than has ever been taken from the earth.*
>
> ***– Napoleon Hill***

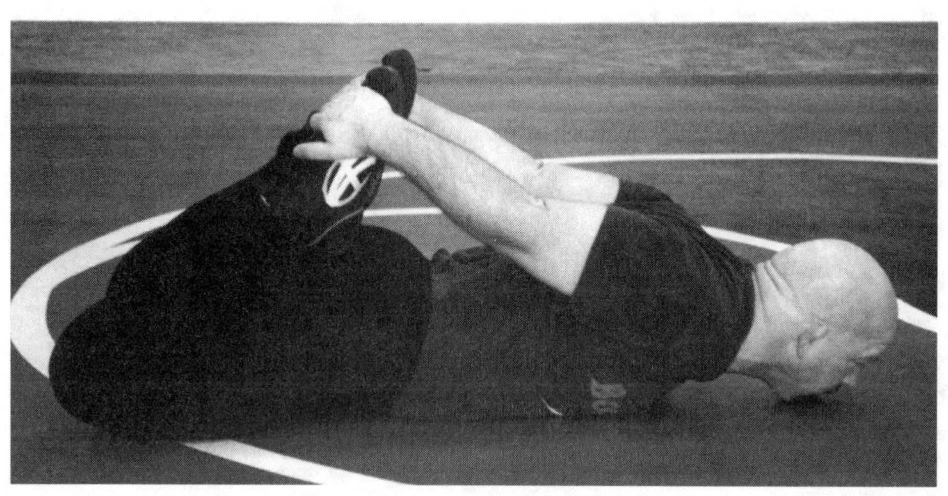

Grab Ankles Lift

Doing this exercise stretches and strengthens the muscles along the spine. One of the other things you can do from this position is use your abdominals as if they are a pair feet. It sounds impossible if you haven't seen it, but I can push my abdominals out while pulling up and as I do so, I bounce off the floor. Anyway, the instructions for this lift are as follows:

1. Lie on the floor with your stomach facing down.
2. Bend your legs backward. Reach back and grab them with your hands.
3. Simultaneously pull your torso and thighs off the ground.
4. Hold the position for three deep breaths.
5. Relax and repeat.

Wrestling writer and historian, Mike Chapman, in referring to the legendary Dan Gable, who won Olympic gold in 1972, once told me the following as we looked at photos of Gable on the victory stand in Munich:

Matt, do you see that look on Gable's face? Do you see the focus? Well, let me tell you a little story. A week later, when he was back in Ames, Iowa, for a celebration following his victory, he still had the exact same look. It hadn't changed a bit. That's how intense his mental focus was.

– from Matt Furey's daily email tips - free at MattFurey.com

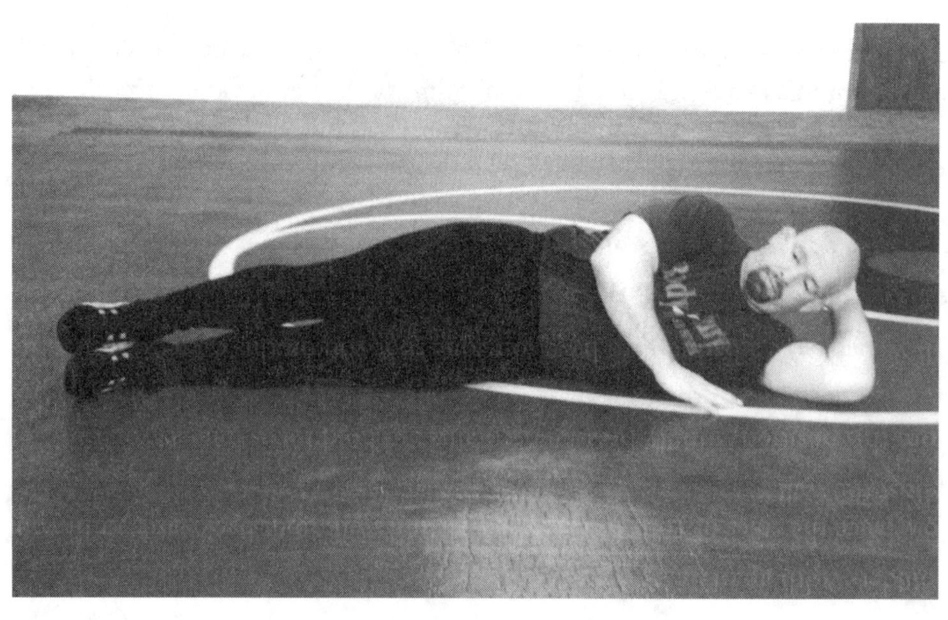

Sideward Leg Lifts

Sideward leg lifts develop strength and flexibility in the hips and thighs. You'll find them much more enjoyable than single leg lifts.

1. Lie on your side with your legs together.
2. Lift both legs off the floor at the same time.
3. Inhale up, exhale down.
4. Do this exercise until fatigued.

Nothing splendid has ever been achieved except by those who dared believe that something inside them was superior to circumstances.

– Bruce Barton

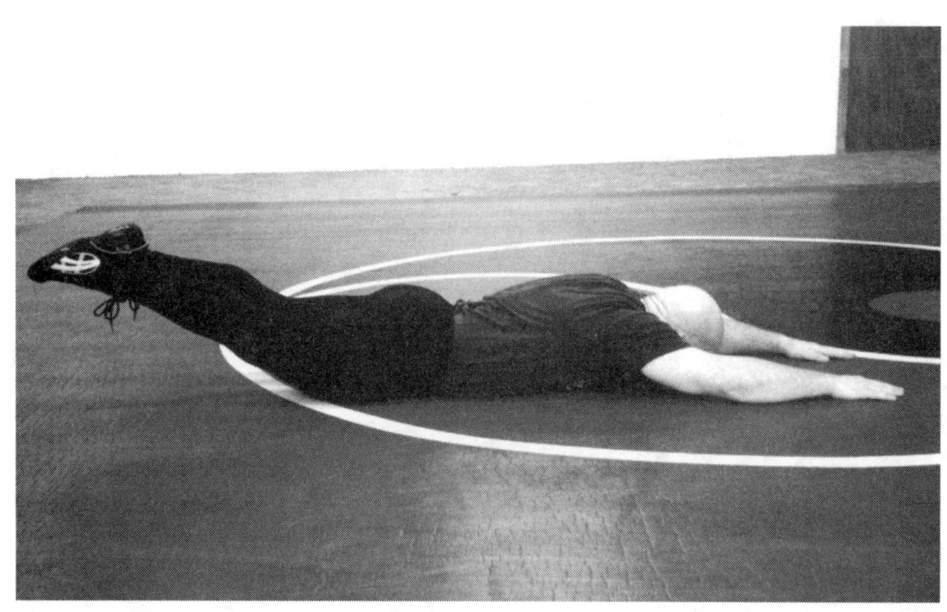

Reverse Leg Lifts

Reverse leg lifts develop strength in the abdominals, lower back and buttocks. You also get a good stretch for the lower back when you do this.

1. Lie face down on the floor with your arms stretched forward.
2. Inhale and lift both legs at the same time. Hold for a couple seconds.
3. Exhale and lower to the floor.
4. Repeat until fatigued.

Torso Lifts

After doing the reverse leg lifts, focus your attention on your upper half. Notice how much your abdominals, hips and back come into play in this exercise.

1. Lie face down on the floor with your arms stretched forward.
2. Inhale and lift your arms, chest and abdominals as high as you can.
3. Exhale and lower to the floor.
4. Repeat until fatigued.

How To Get More Done in Less Time

Want to know the secret of getting more done in less time? Okay, great. Let me give you three things you can do to double your "done" rate.

***Number one**, make out your typical "to do" list before bed each night – or upon arising. You may not think you have time for this, but studies prove those who spend 15 minutes planning their day get back 2 hours in greater productivity.*

***Number two**, highlight the tasks you have to do that are "important" but not urgent. These are the tasks that build a great career, but never fall onto the "urgent" list because… they don't really NEED to be done. Believe me, it was never an "urgent" task for me to write* **Combat Conditioning**. *It's never an "urgent" task for me to exercise. And it's never an "urgent" task for me to hug my wife and children.*

Yet, these things are "important" to me and when I do them, not only do I benefit, others do, too.

***Number three**, do the "important" tasks that you've highlighted and find other people to help you do the "urgent." In fact, the less you do of the "urgent" – the more time you'll spend on the truly important – and the more you and the world will benefit.*

***Last of all**, never forget that daily exercise falls into the "Important" category. You don't have to do it. You can put it off forever. But doing so not only leads to health problems, it leads to far, far less ability to "get things done." Remember, 15 minutes of* **Combat Conditioning** *per day don't just get you into kick butt shape – they give many people as much as two extra hours of increased productivity.*

– from Matt Furey's daily email tips - free at MattFurey.com

Arms Extended Pushups

This exercise works the muscles of the arms, chest, shoulders and abdominals, not to mention the upper and lower back. Strive to get just one of these with your arms fully extended. If you can't, then continue moving your arms back until you find a position that will work.

1. Lie on your stomach with your arms stretched straight in front of you. Your hands are closer together than in a regular pushup.
2. Push everything but your hands and feet off the floor.
3. Lower yourself to the floor and repeat as many times as possible.
4. If you can only do one repetition, hold yourself in the up position as long as you can.
5. If you are unable to even do one repetition, continue pushing as if you can. This resistance will build strength.
6. Breathe naturally throughout this movement.

One-Legged Squats

Once you have built a good deal of lower body strength through Hindu squats and Hindu jumpers, you'll want to give one-legged squats a whirl. They add resistance to your regular squats and help increase leg strength and balance.

1. Stand on one leg with the opposite leg extended forward at waist level. Your hands are stretched straight in front of your chest.
2. Slowly lower your buttocks until they go below your knees.
3. Push back up.
4. Inhale down, exhale up.
5. Do as many repetitions as you can, then switch legs.

> *Nurture great thoughts, for you will never go higher than your thoughts.*
>
> ***– Benjamin Disraeli***

One-Arm Pushups

Like one-legged squats, one-arm pushups add resistance, making your job a lot more difficult. In addition to increased strength in the upper body, one-arm pushups are good for your balance.

1. Stretch out on the floor with your legs spread wide.
2. Rest on the palm of one hand and put the other behind your back.
3. Lower your nose down toward your hand. Push back up.
4. Do as many repetitions as you can.
5. Inhale down, exhale up.

> *Monkeys and apes that climb trees for a living work with their own bodyweight. They don't lift weights or use machines. And so, is it any wonder that a 60 pound chimpanzee has triple the strength of an athletic male – while a gorilla has the strength of 10 Olympic weight lifters?*
>
> ***– from a Matt Furey article***

Towel Pushing

This is an exercise that can only be done on a surface that allows you to slide. It works your entire body with a special amount of stress placed on the abdominals, lower back, shoulders, arms and chest. Work into this one slowly. Talk about a workout.

1. From a standing position, lean forward and place the palms of your hands on the towel placed in front of your feet.
2. Keep your attention focused on your abdominal center.
3. Slowly push the towel forward while keeping your arms straight.
4. Continue pushing until your body is fully extended, but still off the ground.
5. Put your knees on the floor. Using your abdominal muscles, pull backward until your hands are next to your knees.
6. Breathe naturally throughout this movement.
7. Repeat five to ten times.

You've got to be like a horse with blinders on. No matter how tough it is, no matter how hard, you stay focused on your goal. Pay no attention to the distractions to each side of you. Just focus straight ahead at the target you want.

– from Matt Furey's daily email tips - free at MattFurey.com

Penetration Step Lunges

In the art of wrestling, one of the skill development exercises is called a penetration step drill. Most of the time, however, the student is taught to bang one knee into the soft mat. For the purpose of this exercise, we will observe the method employed by old-time American catch-as-catch-can wrestlers, who did not hit a knee when attacking someone's legs. When you perform this exercise the way the old-time wrestlers did it, you'll feel every muscle in your legs (and your buttocks) screaming with delight. This exercise stretches the quadriceps, glutes and hamstrings and promotes explosive strength while building higher levels of lung power.

1. Stand in a staggered wrestler's stance.
2. Take another step forward with the leg you are leading with.
3. Lower your elevation as you step forward. Move forward, almost like the duck waddle. Be careful not to touch your knee on the floor.
4. As the one knee avoids contact with the floor, the other leg steps through.
5. Repeat on the other side, then go back to the original side again.
6. Breathe naturally as you move.
7. Shoot for 15-25 repetitions at first. Eventually 50 or more will be no problem.

A Sample From the Matt Furey Inner Circle @ www.MattFureyInnerCircle.com

What About The Sauna?

Did you know that your skin is the largest eliminative "organ" in the human body? It's true. It covers far more space than your intestines. That's why one of the healthiest things you can do for yourself is "take a sauna." If you're not breaking a sweat each and every day, your body is warehousing far more "waste" than it needs. If you break a sweat each day, you help eliminate excess toxins from the body. But, even if you are breaking a daily sweat, a sauna is still in order as it will force a lot more impurities out of your body – and much faster. I like to sauna several times a week. My son, Frank, who turns 4 in June – takes it with me. I don't let him stay in very long – just enough to crack a good sweat. But the quiet time we have together inside the box is priceless. – When you're in the "hot box" you can practice your deep breathing, do isometrics, do the "theatre of the mind" exercise, a la ***Psycho-Cybernetics****. You can also count your blessings, meditate or quietly reflect upon your life and how you want to improve it. Saunas are also good for weight loss. If you'd like, I can post more information on the type of sauna I use and why. Let me know.*

– M.F.

Pleasant Valleys

After a few rounds of this exercise you may feel that it has been improperly named. Some people prefer to call this exercise "Death Valleys." Nothing could be further from the truth. This exercise may hurt a bit, but it'll give you a reason to live.

1. Sit on the floor with your back straight and your arms overhead.
2. Raise both legs in the air and begin bicycling with your feet.
3. As you bicycle with your feet, imagine you are picking cherries from a tree and dropping them into a bucket behind your head. Squeeze and pull each cherry from the tree. Grip and release, going from one cherry to the next. Keep pedaling your bicycle as you do this.
4. Keep your back straight and breathe naturally.
5. Do 25-200 repetitions of this exercise.

> *For every minute that you are angry, you lose sixty seconds of happiness.*
>
> ***– Emerson***

Head Stand With Neck Stretches

The following exercise stretches and strengthens the sides, front and back of your neck like nothing else. Make sure you begin slowly and only go as far as your body will allow. Don't force anything. Eventually you'll be able to touch your ear to the mat on each side. Once again, as in all the exercises, concentrate on the muscles you are working.

1. Place your head on a soft mat about one foot from a wall.
2. Jump into a head stand. Keep your hands on the mat for balance.
3. Slowly stretch your neck to the front, trying to touch your nose to the mat. Relax and repeat five to ten times.
4. Now slowly go backward. Only goes as far as your body will allow. Relax and repeat five to ten times.
5. Now slowly move toward the left ear. Return to center and move toward the right ear. Repeat five to ten times.
6. Breathe naturally.

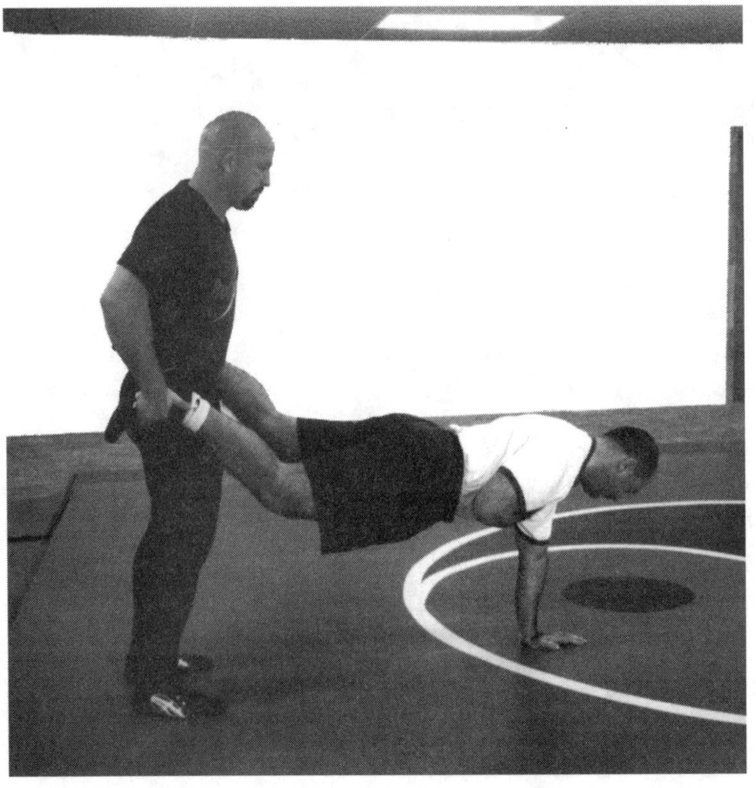

Wheelbarrow walking

Wheelbarrow walking is an exercise in which you will need a partner. It is great for developing strength and endurance throughout the upper body.

1. Have your partner lie face down on the floor.
2. Reach down and grab his ankles.
3. Pull his ankles up to your waist.
4. Your partner now comes off his chest and puts all of his weight on his palms.
5. He now walks forward, and you follow.
6. You can also have him go left and right.
7. Breathe naturally throughout this movement.
8. Continue until fatigued, then switch partners.

Variation: To make this exercise harder, see picture #2, where Gary Long lifts one hand to his chest, then puts it back down and repeats on the other side. This minor variation makes it much, much harder.

Everyone can become a totally focused, driven, motivated goal – achieving machine. It's all in how you use your mind – it's all in what you DO on a regular basis – and it's all in whom you spend your time with. If you spend your time with do-nothings, know-nothings and big talkers, you won't accomplish much. If, on the other hand, you become very selective with whom you will associate with – and only choose winners, you will naturally start to catapult upward, even when you may not consciously think you are trying to do so.

– from Matt Furey's daily email tips - free at MattFurey.com

Jumping Rope

Jumping rope has long been considered one of the very best developers of cardiovascular fitness. It has been said that 10 minutes of jumping rope gives your heart the same benefit as you would get from 30 minutes of running. Based upon this study, you not only save 20 minutes, but your entire body is exercised in a way that you cannot duplicate while running. There are many routines you can follow when jumping rope. The main thing to remember is that you want to continually try to do more complicated exercises. At first it may be difficult to simply jump with both feet together. After awhile, though, this will be easy, so you'll want to run in place while you jump. Or you'll want to alternate jumping: first on one foot, then the other. At any rate, once you're able to do 500 or more consecutive jumps, you're ready to follow the program listed below.

One minute - Jumping rope at fast pace - 150 jumps or more per minute

30 seconds rest

Two minutes - Jumping rope at fast pace - 150 jumps or more per minute

60 seconds rest

Three minutes - Jumping rope at fast pace - 150 jumps or more per minute

60 seconds rest

Two minutes - Jumping rope at fast pace - 150 jumps or more per minute

30 seconds rest

One minute - Jumping rope at fast pace - 150 jumps or more per minute

Altogether this workout represents nine minutes of fast-paced jumping and three minutes of rest. It is a great workout you can do to pick yourself up when feeling blah or as a warm-up before doing other exercises.

Hill Sprints

One exercise that is guaranteed to kick your butt into shape is hill sprints. I used them before going to China to win the world kung fu title in 1997. I first learned of their value when reading about NFL superstars Walter Payton and Marcus Allen, who used them to build explosive speed, power and endurance. Hill sprints have also been used by wrestlers all over the world. If you live in an area that doesn't have hills, then run the stairs at a football stadium, basketball arena or some other place.

When you first begin running hill sprints, you'll only need a hill that is about 50 to 70 yards long. Do not go out and try to tackle a hill that is a two miles long. The key is sprinting, not long distance running. Eventually, as you get used to running hill sprints, you can vary the distance. You can start off with 50 yards and work up to 150 yards or more. It's up to you. The key is doing them three days a week.

When you do a hill sprint, do not run back down the hill. Take your time and walk back down. This allows you to catch your breath and to concentrate all your energies on each burst. Also, running down hill can be hard on the joints.

Here is a sample program:

Monday

Five 50-yard hill sprints

Wednesday

Three 50-yard hill sprints
Two 70-yard sprints
Two 90-yard sprints

Friday

One 150-yard sprint
One 100-yard sprint
One 80-yard sprint
One 70-yard sprint
One 60-yard sprint
Three 50-yard sprints

Uphill Buddy Carries

Just when you thought that hill sprints took the cake, you have someone who comes up with Uphill Buddy Carries. That someone, by the way, IS NOT ME. When I was training under Dan Gable at the University of Iowa, we had to carry our training partner up the steps of the arena ... and that was at the end of practice, when our tails were really dragging.

Naturally, with someone on your back, you won't be able to run too fast uphill (or up a long flight of stairs), but your muscles will get the point anyway.

The key is finding someone of comparable weight. If you weigh 150 pounds, you don't want to carry a 300-pounder uphill, believe me. At the same time though, if no one your size is around, carrying a lighter person will still make life rough for you.

In terms of a routine, uphill buddy carries are really more of an exercise that you do AFTER hill sprints. Carrying your partner up the hill one to three times should be enough.

Here are some instructions on how to do Uphill Buddy Carries:

1. Squat down enough for your partner to jump on your back.
2. Have your partner drape his arms over your shoulders.
3. Your arms are under his legs. Reach up with your hands and your partner reaches down to meet you. Clasp hands.
4. Keep your head up and begin a slow trot up the hill. Your goal is to go the whole way without stopping.
5. Breathe naturally as you go.
6. Do one to three rounds, alternating after each time or going straight through.

Road Work

A lot of athletes mistakenly believe that cardiovascular conditioning is the key to maintaining energy in a combat sport. Hence, they think that running mile after mile is a good idea. Not true. There is nothing wrong with running, but in combat sports like wrestling and in mixed martial arts competitions (often referred to as no-holds-barred fighting), you do not fight standing up the entire time. You fight in many different positions, at different speeds and with varying degrees of muscular effort. This variety helps explain exactly why wrestling and mixed martial arts competitions are not "cardio." Sure, some of your training can be running, but much better than running is what Karl Gotch calls "road work."

By "road work" Karl means that you work (or workout) while running along the road. Instead of running two to five miles, try throwing punches while you run. That alone will make you realize how different fighting is from running. Other things you can do while running are pushups, duck waddling, bear crawls, Hindu squats, and so on.

"Expect the unexpected," says Karl. "Visualize your opponent while you train and imagine that each time you do road work you have a different opponent in front of you. No match is ever exactly the same, so never do road work in exactly the same manner."

I think the quote in the above paragraph pretty much says it all. But there is one more thing: When you do road work, wear combat boots.

The fastest way there is to get fit is a combination of bodyweight calisthenics as seen in my book and videos on ***Combat Conditioning*** *– as well as the hill sprints I write about on page 117. But the thing most people MUST understand is this: If you are currently in poor condition, it is not wise to go outside and begin running sprints right away. You need to work into it. If you are in poor condition and you start cranking out sprints, the chances of pulling a hamstring are quite high.*

Running HILL sprints (as opposed to sprints on flat ground) helps dramatically reduce the chance of a hamstring pull because it is much harder to build up the speed necessary to hurt yourself. Hill sprints also increase strength in your legs and lungs much more than flat land sprints. And so, if you want to get the benefits of hill sprinting when you're not in condition, what should you do. Here is a sample progression for you:

1. Briskly walk up the hill. A brisk walk is much harder than you think – and far different from a "stroll."

2. When the brisk walk becomes easy, run up the hill.

3. When running up the hill gets easy, sprint up the hill.

If you don't have hills, then follow the same training philosophy when you train on flat land, or on soft sandy beaches, or in the pool… on an exercise bike – and so on.

– from a Matt Furey article

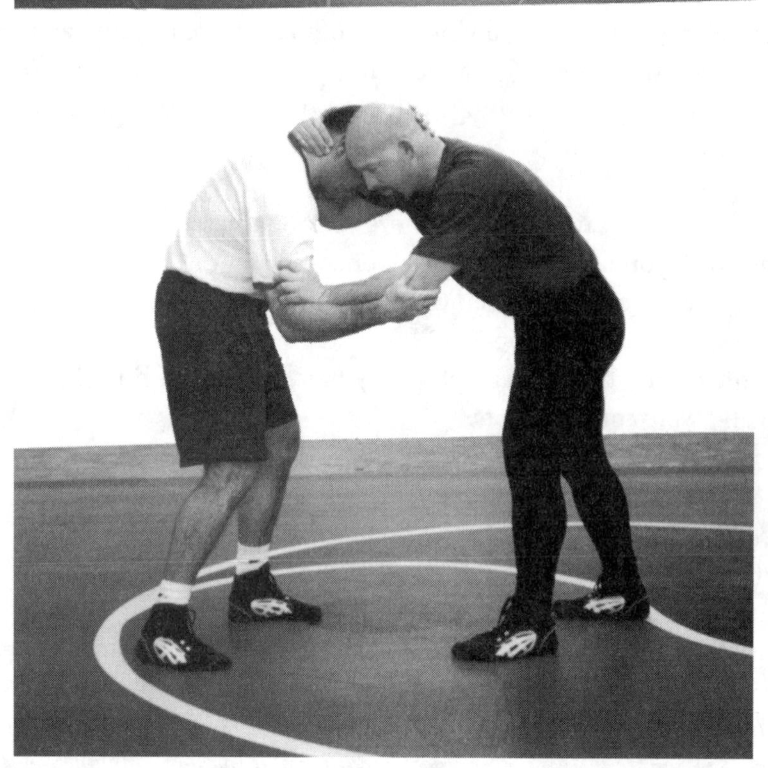

Wrestling

There are a great many combat sports that you can participate in. All of them can greatly improve your conditioning level. In addition to wrestling, I have practiced tai chi, various styles of kung fu and boxing. But nothing, in my estimation, develops the mind and body like wrestling.

When I speak of wrestling, I am speaking of it in all its forms and guises, including freestyle, Greco-Roman, judo, jiu-jitsu, Brazilian jiu-jitsu, sambo, shuai-chiao and my favorite, catch-as-catch-can. All of these combat sports/martial arts are great training, physically, mentally and spiritually. They develop the human being to levels he never dreamed possible.

Once thought of as the "manly art" - wrestling is now enjoying increased popularity among women as well. The world over, wrestlers have always been the best conditioned athletes. They don't have the muscles of a bodybuilder or power lifter, but they have the functional strength that no bodybuilder or power lifter can match. Many of these muscle boys have come into the wrestling room or dojo and left with bruised egos. It isn't easy facing the reality that a 20-inch arm may be impressive to look at, but a muscle guy with big arms still can't beat a grappler who really knows how to use every square inch of his body.

If you are not involved in one of the wrestling arts listed above, I recommend that you first begin with the exercises in this book. Conditioning is the best hold you can learn. Once you have attained a basic level of fitness, then you're ready to begin learning and without great fear of injury due to weakness, inflexibility or lousy lung power.

If you are already involved in a combat sport, be it a wrestling art or a striking art such as karate, boxing, kung fu or the like, the exercises in this book are for you as well. If you haven't been doing exercises like this, chances are you are not in condition, even if you have been involved in your art for years. There are plenty of so-called combat athletes. You don't want to be one of them. Be a conditioned combat athlete. There is a world of difference between the two.

Even if you have never been involved in a combat art, and never plan to be, the exercises in this book are the greatest gift I can give you. Health, as the saying goes, is our greatest wealth.

Last of all, if you are interested in catch wrestling, be sure to visit **www.farmerburns.com**

Sample Combat Conditioning Routines

Each of the following programs can be done as a single workout or in combination with another workout. For example, you can do the Hindu Squat and pushup workout during the same training session. But there is nothing wrong with doing one workout in the morning and another later in the day. Figure out what works best for you and take it from there.

Look through this book and choose three to five exercises, or more, and create your own routine out of them. Some days you'll only want to do bridging, Hindu squats and Hindu pushups. On other days you can put together a workout of 15 or 20 different exercises, but done with less intensity than on other days.

The keys to success in ***Combat Conditioning*** are hard work, a "have fun" mindset and variety in what you do. If you always do the same workout, the training can become dull. When you switch things around, even a little bit, you'll realize that a slight change in a routine can make a big difference.

I Want, I Want, I Want

When it comes to making changes and achieving goals in your life, the process is actually quite simple. We complicate the matter by – well, complicating the matter. So let's take something basic and simple you do everyday and analyze the "success" process. Each and every day of your life you "get hungry." And when you get hungry you ask yourself "What do I want to eat?" After asking this question your brain scans the data and comes up with a mental image of a specific food. Once you see that image in your mind you say something like this, "Yeah, I want that." Then guess what you do? You get up off your ass and do whatever it takes to eat the food that you chose. – Now, in case you think this is overly simplistic, you're right. And this exact sequence is precisely what you go through when you want to accomplish matters more serious than your next meal. Ask yourself, "What do I want?" Once you get the answer in the form of a mental image, mentally choose it by saying, "Yes, I want that." Then do whatever it takes to bring it into your reality.

– More to come. M.F.

500 Hindu Squats Workout

Do five sets of 80 regular Hindu Squats followed by 20 Hindu Jump Squats. Focus on your breathing while you train. Exhale when you go down, inhale when you come up. After each 100 you may run in place to help your legs recover, but do not stand around or sit down. Keep moving. This keeps your heart rate elevated and helps you maintain your focus and intensity.

Hindu Squats

Hindu Jump Squats

250 Pushups Workout

In this workout you will do a variety of different pushups, one after the other. Listed below is a sample of how you can do this program.

100 Hindu Pushups
10 Fingertip Pushups
10 Reverse Pushups
30 Hindu Pushups
20 Fingertip Pushups
30 Hindu Pushups
20 One Leg in Air Pushups
10 Fingertip Pushups
20 Hindu Pushups

When doing the Hindu pushups you will inevitably hit a sticking point where you cannot do another one. Do your best to rest in the up position with your butt in the air and all weight still centered over your hands. Catch your breath and continue. Training this way builds more endurance, not to mention mental toughness.

Hindu Pushups

Reverse Pushups

One Leg Pushups

Fingertip Pushups

The Karl Gotch Bible

This is a great workout that combines squats and pushups via the use of a deck of cards. The Japanese wrestlers Karl Gotch trained referred to this as the Karl Gotch Bible. Here is how it works. Get a deck of cards out, shuffle them well and start dealing. When you deal a number card in red, do that many Hindu pushups. If you get a face card, do 10-15 pushups. For the black cards do Hindu squats. Jokers are wild, giving 20 reps. Continue dealing until you've gone through the entire deck. It's one of the best workouts you can do and all you need for equipment is 54 cards.

Hindu Push-ups v. Dive Bomber Push-ups ... Which Is Better?

One of the biggest myths about Hindu push-ups (also known as dand) is that they are the same as the Dive Bomber Push-up, often done in the military. Not true at all.

Many years ago, before I learned the proper form for Hindu push-ups, I thought they were the same, too. And my ignorance was bliss until I fell under the guiding eye and thunderous voice of Karl Gotch.

Even though I have taught the proper form for Hindu Push-ups in my ***Combat Conditioning book and videos*** *– and even though hundreds of thousands of people from all over the world are now doing this style of push-up, including the military, the myth still persists. In fact, one of those bothersome Frequently Asked Questions is, "When I do Hindu push-ups, do I bend my arms again after finishing the first part of the movement, or do I just push back to the start?"*

The answer is: You simply push back to the start. You do NOT bend your arms a second time.

Therein lies the primary difference between the dand and the Dive-Bomber. When doing dive-bomber push-ups, you bend your arms in the first part of the movement and once again in the second. No doubt, bending twice does cause more arm pump – but don't be misled into thinking that this makes them better than Hindu push-ups. Not a chance.

Walking, One-Legged Squats and Reverse Pushups

This workout consists of three exercises that will hit almost every muscle in your body. Begin by walking backwards down the wall and coming back up ten times. After that, do a couple sets of one-legged squats, ten each leg. Then finish off with five sets of reverse pushups, doing as many as you can in each set.

Wall Walk

One Legged Squats

Reverse Pushups

Scab Run

The scab run is one of those regimens I learned while at the University of Iowa. One of the wrestling coaches, Keith Mourlam (nicknamed Scab), used to do this run a lot so we named it after him. I have modified it a bit but the idea is still the same. Do not do this workout if you have eaten in the last five hours. It'll get your insides churning, that's for sure.

Sprint 100 yards
25 pushups

Sprint 100 yards
25 pushups

Sprint 80 yard
25 leg lifts

Sprint 80 yards
25 leg lifts

Sprint 60 yards
25 squats

Sprint 60 yards
25 squats

Sprint 40 yards
25 v-ups

Sprint 40 yards
25 v-ups

Sprint 20 yards
25 pushups

Sprint 20 yards
25 pushups

Circuit training

When most people think of circuit training, they usually associate it with weights. But try it with ***Combat Conditioning*** exercises and see what you think. Basically, what you do is jump rope or run in place for one minute after doing a set of calisthenics. Then you go on and do another series of calisthenics, and so on, until you've had enough. One round of what is listed below will definitely get your attention. As you get into better shape, though, you can do two or three rounds with more repetitions in each exercise. Adapt and improvise. Make it hard and keep it interesting.

Hindu Squats - 50
One minute rope skipping

Hindu Pushups - 25
One minute rope skipping

V-ups - 25
One minute rope skipping

Reverse pushups - 10
One minute rope skipping

No momentum situps - 10
One minute rope skipping

Table Making - 20
One minute rope skipping

Kneeling backbend - 10
One minute rope skipping

Hindu Squats

Hindu Pushups

V – ups

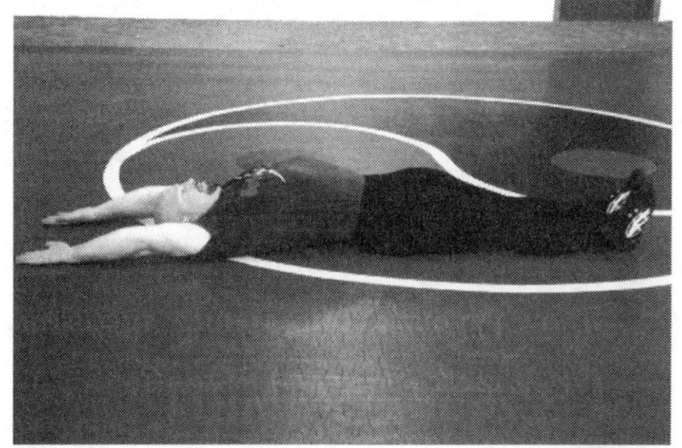

Reverse Pushups

No Momentum Sit-ups

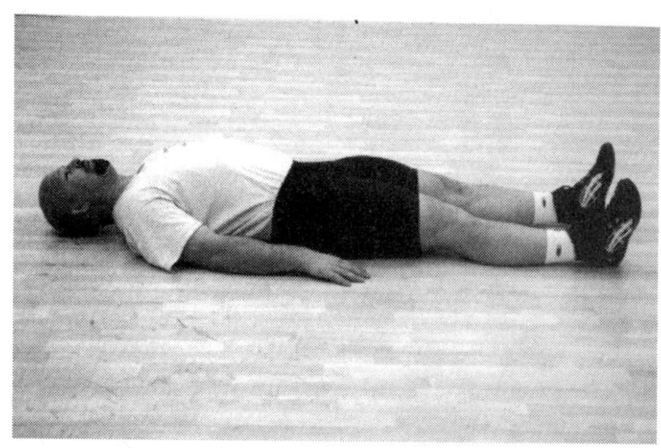

Table Making

Kneeling Back Bend

In the olden days, whenever you heard about someone tearing their rotator cuff, you automatically assumed it must be a Big Leauge pitcher. Not anymore. Rotator cuff injuries are very common in most sports today,as well as in the weight room.

The reasons:

#1. *Reliance on the bench press as a measure of upper body strength or to build big pecs. Danger: In building the pecs, the shoulder is compromised. This unnatural lift leaves many powerful men crippled as they age. Their rotator cuff is literally shot - and sometimes on BOTH shoulders.*

#2. *Failure to do natural bodyweight movements that strengthen the shoulders beyond belief. What 'natural' bodyweight movements are these?*

Answer: *Handstand pushups – along with a variety of other exercises done from a handstand position. Handstand work used to be a 'staple' in the training repertoire of all series fitness enthusiasts. Then the tee-vee arrived and the butt-flop took its place – along with the bench press. Between the two, sitting on your 'arse' and lying on your back to do bench presses, we've got a nation of virtual weaklings. Want real upper body strength? Then train yourself with handstand pushups and other handstand exercises. Avoid the bench press like the plague. It's just NOT good for you.*

– from a Matt Furey article

The Most Neglected Muscle in the Body

..987, during my first year in the biz of personal fitness training, I had an 18-year old client named Tim.

He was gung-ho at first. Showed up on time. Worked his arse off. Never complained.

Then, all of a sudden, after about five weeks, he started to miss workouts. Despite my "rah rah" talks with him his behavior didn't change. In fact, it got worse. Seven weeks into the program and he dropped out. No phone call. No explanation. Would not return my calls.

A couple years later, from "out of the blue" Tim called again. He wanted to come back.

Upon starting back up he explained that the reason he dropped out before was due to his problems with alchohol and drugs. Now that he was "clean and sober" – all was well. There weren't going to be any problems.

But… true to form, despite giving up the booze and dope, five weeks into the program and Tim's behavior started to look the same. He missed a Monday workout – and showed up late on Wednesday.

This time I gave no "rah rah" talk. I simply confronted Tim and asked him a number of questions about why he was missing sessions and coming late. Tim's response was as follows: "It's raining. I don't feel motivated when it's raining."

"What makes you think you need to be motivated?" I asked.

Tim had no answer for this one. It was sort of a brain-bender.

So I followed up with, "Which would you rather be – motivated or focused?"

Tim replied, "Focused."

"That's right," I said. "Now, what's more important to you, staying home when it's raining or getting your body in great shape?"

"Getting in great shape," said Tim.

"Right again," I said. "Now, how about this. From now on, do me a favor: Whenever you come up with an excuse for why you don't want to train, I want you to ask yourself this question: 'What do I want most, to do 'X' or to get into great shape?' If you do this, I think you'll always be focused."

Tim agreed to do as I requested. Six months later he was still with me. He never missed another workout. And he got into kick-butt shape.

Yes, I know what I just described seems simple. But the best things in life are just that: SIMPLE.

It all boils down, once again, to the questions you ask yourself: Do you WANT to get fit? Do you really, really, really WANT to get fit?

Questions focus your mind better than anything.

Strengthen your WANT muscle and your body will follow.

Kick ass – take names!

Matt Furey

P.S.: By the way, if you want to achieve every fitness goal you've ever set, as well as every other goal that is important to you, then it's time to give your WANT muscle the kick-start it deserves. Quit hemmin and hawin. Go to ***www.MattFurey.com*** right now and sign up for my **free** daily fitness tips.

Commonly Asked Questions

1. How often should I train?

How often should you bathe? How often should you eat? Follow animals in the wild. They don't exercise once or twice a week. Exercise is a necessity for survival. Human beings, on the other hand, are always looking for the easy way out and that's why most are ready for the scrap heap before the age of 30. Take care of your body. The greatest wealth is health. My advice is simple: Do a few of the exercises in this book every day. Work harder some days than others, but do something everyday.

2. Can I do the squats and pushups and bridging everyday?

Yes, you can. I'm not saying you have to, but you sure can. ***Combat Conditioning*** is not like bodybuilding, where you train certain body parts one day and others the next. Take monkeys and other primates that climb trees for a living. They don't follow a three-day split. They don't use creatine or take liquid amino acids each day. They don't follow muscle confusion principles. They do the same type of exercises each day and they're far stronger than human beings.

3. How long should my workout last?

That all depends upon your goals and the time you have available each day. You might train 15 minutes and you might train for a couple hours or more. It all depends upon why you're training. Combat athletes will spar and practice the elements of their sports in addition to these exercises. But the regular man or woman interested in being physically fit will probably not want to spend that much time, but he or she can still get amazing results without investing a lot of time. Make no mistake about it though, everyone has some time each day for training. If you can't make 15 to 30 minutes per day for exercise, then I suggest you reevaluate your life and what you're doing with it. If health reigns supreme, then get up off your ass and train a bit each day. Even if all you have time for is some light stretching and deep breathing exercises, that goes a lot further than plopping in front of the boob tube and wondering why you don't have any energy.

4. I only have 15 minutes a day, what can I do in that amount of time?

In 15 minutes you can do 500 Hindu squats. In and of themselves, the Hindu squats are a great workout. You're not only working your legs, buttocks and lower back, but the deep breathing and swinging of the arms develops lung power and strength throughout the rest of your body. You can also take five or six exercises and do quite a number of each, and that would be your routine. For example, you could start with walking the wall five times, then you could do 100 Hindu squats, then 50 Hindu pushups, then 25 leg lifts and 10 reverse pushups. That is a good workout and it won't take long at all.

5. I travel a lot. Is this program something I can do in my hotel room?

Absolutely, and that is one of the great things about it. You don't need equipment, yet you'll get more benefits in terms of strength, endurance and flexibility than if you spend the day in a health club loaded with tens of thousands of dollars worth of mechanical equipment.

6. I still like to lift weights, is that okay?

Sure, it's okay. Stick with what you like to do. Some of the people I have coached do the Hindu squats, pushups and bridging on the days in which they don't lift weights. I used to lift weights but since I began the ***Combat Conditioning*** I have never looked back. I have gotten the greatest benefit from these exercises, but that's me. Other people are different. The most important thing is that you do some form of exercise on a regular basis.

7. How much stronger can I expect to get from a program of calisthenics as opposed to super slow weight training or some of the other programs?

That all depends upon how much effort you put into it and how consistent you are in your routines. But to give you an idea, let me tell you the following story. Steve Maxwell, a good friend of mine, owns a gym in Philadelphia called **Maxercise**. He is a world champion in Brazilian Jiu-Jitsu as well as a personal trainer. He follows the ***Combat Conditioning*** exercises I teach and has his jiu-jitsu students doing them as well. But for his clients in personal training, he has most of them use the machines. Well, one guy came to him for help that had been getting trained elsewhere on the weights. He was really weak and Steve decided to do something different. He started him on a program that consisted of Hindu squats, Hindu pushups, bridging, pullups, situps and the like. Trouble was that the client couldn't do any of these exercises well. He couldn't even do ten straight squats, or five pushups, or one pullup, and so on. Within ninety days the guy was doing hundreds of squats in a row, ten pullups, holding a bridge for three minutes and cracking off 50 pushups. His physical appearance completely changed and Steve decided to test him on the weights. It turns out the guy was now far stronger on the weights than he had been when training elsewhere. And this was without weight training. When Steve told me this story I said to him, "And guess what would have happened if you did the reverse?"

"What do you mean?" Steve asked.

"Well, what if you had the guy on all the machines for 90 days and then tested him in squats, pushups, pullups, bridging and situps?"

"Oh, I see your point," said Steve. "He still wouldn't be able to do them."

"Right," I said.

I hope this gives you some insight into how effective these calisthenics are.

Let me say this to close out my answer: Don't be lazy. Work on these calisthenics even if you're currently not very athletic, and within 90 days you're going to be a whole new person.

8. What do you think of aerobic exercise equipment?

Most aerobic exercise machines are okay and they are helpful to people who need to rehabilitate injuries or those who cannot go outside to walk, run or do other forms of exercise. But I think you should avoid them as much as you can. Learn to do things the natural way.

9. Do you do any stretching before you do the exercises?

No. Stretching is good but it isn't necessary to do stretches before doing these exercises simply because most of them are simultaneously strengthening your body while stretching it out. There are a lot of stretches you can do after the exercises are finished and in the future I will put out a stretching course, but for now you have plenty of work to do, so don't worry.

10. My knees hurt when I do the squats. Any suggestions?

First of all, before doing any of these exercises, remember that they are for people in good health and that you should never engage in any exercise program without the consent of your physician. With that said, you'll want to check your form. You may be leaning forward too far. Keep your back straight when you go down and when you come back up. If the knee pain persists, keep your heels flat when you go down. Almost without exception, knee pain when doing the squats is a result of having weak tendons and ligaments. Once these get built up you'll be fine.

11. I was in a car accident a few months ago and hurt my neck and back very badly. Is it okay for me to do the bridge?

That all depends upon the health of your spine right now. Don't do anything without the approval of your physician.

12. What do you think of swimming?

Swimming is a great exercise and one of the best you can do. It has a relaxing and calming effect on the body. Unfortunately, those who don't know how will find it complicated to learn. I highly recommend it but make sure you learn the strokes properly. You can certainly put it into your routine with no argument from me. I swam competitively for ten years and know that it works the entire body, from head to toe.

13. What improvements do you think I can expect after a month of *Combat Conditioning*?

Your entire body will be stronger and more flexible. You'll have a lot more endurance and mentally you'll be more focused and alert than ever before. Your confidence will soar as well.

14. You have so many exercises. I'm just a beginner. What should I do to get started?

Remember the Royal Court. Concentrate on Hindu squats, Hindu pushups and bridging. After one solid month of those three, you'll be a new person. You'll also be ready to add some other exercises.

15. Should I exercise in the morning or at night?

In the early morning the air is cleaner so it's a great time to do it. Plus, throughout the rest of the day you can look back with a feeling of accomplishment on what you did. But in the big picture, find a time that works for you and stick with it. If you can't train early in the morning, do it later in the day. Avoid making excuses and you'll be fine.

16. Is it okay to eat before training?

I wouldn't recommend it when you are first learning. After you get into reasonable shape, you can eat some fruit or something light an hour before training and this may prove to be okay for you. Then again, maybe it won't. It's an individual situation and you'll have to monitor how you feel.

17. My wife dumped me for a man with a flat stomach. If I do these exercises do you think I can win her back?

Winning her back may not be what is best. Obviously she has moved on. Concentrate on yourself for now. Perform these exercises and you'll probably attract someone into your life who is much better than what you had. I've seen it happen over and over again. As one door closes another opens.

18. What about alcohol? Can I get sloshed every night and still make progress?

Only in your dreams, pal. Only in your dreams.

19. I noticed that you don't have many pulling type movements in your program. Do you not think they are important?

Pulling movements are important, but you're going to find something out that is a surprise to most people. I want you to work on the handstand pushups until you can pop off 15 of them without any trouble. When you can do that, go test yourself on pull-ups and let me know how well you do. I think you're going to be amazed.

20. When you do roadwork, what kind of shoes do you wear?

I usually wear a pair of army jungle boots. They're comfortable as can be and they absorb shock more than running shoes. They also have the best ankle support you can buy. The army created boots so that soldiers would be able to cross any type of terrain with the least amount of discomfort. I really believe they know what they are doing when it comes to boots and that's why I wear them. Give them a try yourself. They're lighter than you think. Just make sure you break them in real well before your run in them.

A Sneak Peak at other Matt Furey Products

"Five Second Abs... and the Magnificent Seven"

How Seven Old-Time Exercises Burn Fat From Your Waistline in Record Time

By Frank Sherrill

I couldn't believe what I was hearing. The idea was preposterous. Matt Furey, a world champion martial artist and world-renowned fitness guru was telling me that I could "reduce inches from my waistline with a few deep breathing exercises" that he calls ***The Magnificent Seven***.

And get this, one repetition of the deep breathing exercise he recommends most takes only 2 to 5 seconds. **Five second abs???** Was this a lark, or what?

In all my years of doing cardio, pumping iron and generally depriving myself, no one ever told me that deep breathing exercises alone could greatly ramp up my metabolism, turning me into a fat-burning machine.

No one ever told me that one of the main reasons behind cardiovascular exercise was simply to get you breathing harder so that the increased oxygen in your system cranks up your metabolism.

Don't know about you, but due to my skepticism about these claims, I decided to do some research on deep breathing. And to my utter amazement I found that more oxygen in your body equals:

a.) a revved-up metabolism

b.) greater strength and endurance

c.) improved health and...

d.) faster weight loss.

In addition to the above, when you do deep breathing exercises the way Matt Furey teaches in his best-selling ***Combat Abs*** program, you have better circulation, better digestion and an increased ability to handle stress. You have a feeling of calmness and well-being. You look younger, feel better, have a sharper mind... and greater energy.

Now that's a lot of benefits, don't you think?

Those reasons alone were enough for me to **get Furey's program and learn** – but there's more.

Learn What to Eat and What NOT to Eat

In addition to the deep breathing benefits – Furey's ***Combat Abs*** course was unique because it gave me details about his amazing **Furey Fat Loss Program** – a program that helps you lose weight without losing strength or depriving yourself. Matt created it in 1997, on the road to winning his world title in Beijing.

Matt Furey won a national collegiate wrestling title in 1985 and a world shuai-chiao kung fu championship in 1997. Furey has a knack for taking the average and ordinary person and transforming him with his powerful programs. Furey was inducted into the Edinboro University Athletic Hall of Fame in 1998 and spends much time each year traveling throughout the world, searching for the very best information available to his world-wide audience. His website, **www.mattfurey.com**, is one of the finest in the world, giving valuable information that changes lives.

Strong Man Otto Arco trained his abs with his entire body as one unit.

And it works!

In ***Combat Abs*** I also learned a series of **abdominal exercises I could do, get this, while standing on my feet**. I was told that old-time boxers, wrestlers and martial artists had better abs than the athletes of today and they did so without crunches and other lie-down abdominal exercises that most people find boring.

Upon hearing this I began to do some research. I wanted to find these so-called "great abs" legends of yesteryear. To my surprise, I DID find them. You can see what I mean from the photos in this article. Were these guys amazing or what? Furey has really done his research.

Fitness pioneer Maxick developed powerful abs WITHOUT crunches.

So I bought ***Combat Abs***. A few days later, when it arrived in the mail, I ripped open the package and starting rifling through the course. To say I was amazed with what I read would be an understatement.

One Man Took 20" off His Waist

After doing the exercises for a couple days I quickly noticed a change in my waistline. My abs were definitely tighter and harder and my clothes were fitting better. At that point I readily understood why Furey gets so many testimonials for his programs, including the following:

*Using your **Combat Abs** system I have taken 20 full inches off my waist. I look so much better I think that it saved my marriage!*
Sincerely,
Rick Hackworth, Ph.D.

Combat Abs is packed with one ab sculpting and strengthening exercise after another – all systematically taught, so that you can progress from the raw beginner stage to the level of mastery – and quickly, too.

In *Combat Abs* you will learn...

- 7 exercises that will strengthen and tighten your abs like nothing else in the world!
- A deep breathing isometric exercise that tightens and tones your abdominals within days!
- Abdominal exercises that massage your internal organs – and how this aids in losing excess flab!
- The abdominal exercises you MUST do to ensure a healthy pain-free lower back!
- The exercises that make your abs so rock-solid tough that you'll laugh when punched in the midsection!
- The secret to setting, and most importantly, achieving, all your health and fitness goals!
- and much more...

If you've come this far with me, one thing is for certain, you probably want a set of rock-hard abs and a powerful yet lean waistline. So you're now faced with one of two choices:

1. Stop reading this article, watch some tee-vee, do nothing for your body and remain unsatisfied with your appearance.

2. Order your copy of ***Combat Abs*** today and change your life for the better.

I certainly hope you go for option #2 because doing so will give you the waistline you want and deserve.

"Just nodding your head won't row the boat."
Irish proverb

Call (813) 994 8267 to place your order for ***Combat Abs***. Only $29.95 plus $6 S&H U.S. – ($12 S&H foreign). Or visit us online at www.mattfurey.com/combat_abs.html

☐ Yes, send me Matt Furey's best selling book, ***Combat Abs*** for only $29.95 plus $6 S&H ($12 S&H foreign).

NAME: ______

ADDRESS: ______

CITY ______ STATE ______ ZIP ______

COUNTRY: ______ PHONE: ______

☐ Money Order drawn from a U.S. bank

☐ Visa ☐ MasterCard ☐ Amex ☐ Discover

CARD NO: ______

EXP: ______ SIGNATURE: ______

Make Money Order Payable to:
Matt Furey Enterprises, Inc.
10339 Birdwatch Dr., Tampa, Florida 33647, USA
www.mattfurey.com
Phone: (813) 994-8267 • **Fax:** (813) 994-4947

CmbtCndtn

"Before I Learned the Real Secrets to Flexibility I Was Stiff, Tight and Muscle-Bound... But Not Anymore!"

How To Double Your Flexibility In One Evening!!!

Matt Furey doing the front splits with ease, despite having "tree trunk" legs

Follow my step by step program and feel the tight spots loosen, the pain dissipate and the years of stretching frustration waylaid. Amaze your friends with your new found flexibility.

Dear Friend,

Last weekend I was in Cincinnati, having dinner at **TGIFridays** with a group of friends. One of the people at the table was Bill, an executive in his early 40's. He kept asking me about the many coaches I have had throughout my career. He wanted to know what Olympic champion Dan Gable was like. He wanted to know what Bruce Baumgartner (another Olympic champion) was like. He wanted to know what Karl Gotch was like... and so on.

Finally, out of the blue, he asks me, **"Are you flexible?"**

"Sure am," I said, thinking nothing of it. Then I continued: "But I didn't use to be. In fact, I was so stiff I started having back pain in college."

Bill then put a puzzled, I-don't-believe-you look on his face. "**YOU'RE** flexible?" he questioned. "I wouldn't think with your muscular size that you would be."

I proceeded to tell Bill that I could do the splits, hold a gymnastic bridge with one arm, lie on my stomach, grab my ankles and jump off the floor only using my stomach muscles, and so on. He looked at me in surprise and gave me one of those long drawn out words. I'm sure you're familiar with it. It sounds like this...

"REALLLLLY?"

Then it hit me. If this guy doesn't think I'm flexible because of the way I'm built, then there are probably a lot of other people who think the same thing. Moreover and more importantly, these people could greatly benefit from the unique system of stretching I teach.

My system can even help the super stiff double their flexibility—oftentimes in one hour.

Let me tell you about ***Vampiro***, a world famous pro wrestler, and a prime example of someone I have helped gain far more flexibility in one hour than he could attain following other programs for months, even years. I'm sure you're familiar with some of these programs. They're the ones that lead to a destination called... frustration.

Just so you know, ***Vampiro*** is 6'3" and 255 pounds of streaming steel. He is incredibly powerful and quick as a cat. Yet, in terms of flexibility, he has endured so much pain in the ring, including a broken neck, that some of his muscles and joints had no give left in them. Talk about stiff. He had the flexibility of an iron dog. He was even stiffer than I used to be.

Well, a couple months ago ***Vampiro*** came to Tampa to train with me for a few days. When he left he had this to say:

"I just finished my private bootcamp with Matt. Today was great. Wait, today was...emotional. When I came here I wasn't able to come close to touching my nose in the bridge. I was only on the top of my head. But within 30 minutes Matt had me down and touching for the first time. I also had a shoulder injury that was killing me and needed an operation. I couldn't move my right arm without a lot of shoulder pain. Matt fixed it in 6 min.. I also SAW Matt help a guy to breathe that was so sick, he could not even talk! Thank you Matt, from the heart."

Now, bear in mind that I only worked with Vampiro on some of the stretching exercises I'll be teaching you in my new course entitled, ***Combat Stretching – How To Double Your Flexibility In One Evening***. Why? Because he was primarily here to improve his submission fighting skills.

So imagine how fabulous he would have felt if I would have taught him the entire program you'll be learning in my new course. And imagine how great you're going to feel when you impress your friends with your new found flexibility.

This mind-blowing course will consist of three parts, taught on three separate videos. Part one will feature nearly 20 dynamic stretches, many of which most people here in the U.S. have never seen or done before. These dynamic stretches increase flexibility through movement, hitting all the major muscle groups and joints. You'll learn dynamic movements used by Hindu wrestlers as well as some of the toughest champion athletes in Japan and China. **[Don't forget, I live in China during part of each year; my wife is Chinese and I won a world kung fu title in Beijing, so I have access to teachings most Americans would love to know. And I'm bringing them to you in this course.]**

The bottom-line is that you won't just become flexible from these dynamic movements—you'll also get stronger.

Always remember that flexibility without strength is a very bad thing. If you're in a combat sport and you're limber but weak, I think you know what will happen to you. That kind of flexibility makes you injury prone. Not a good thing. So it's important to strike a delicate balance between strength and flexibility. One without the other is not good.

I've said it before and I'll say it again, ***"What does it matter if you have the flexibility to kick someone in the head, if you don't have enough power in the kick to knock him out."***

The dynamic stretches I teach will give you that "moving" functional stretch and the power to go with it.

These dynamic stretches alone will greatly enhance and improve your current level of flexibility. They will also give you more energy, more stamina and increase feelings of well-being. And for those of you who compete in sports, they're the perfect warm-up before engaging in more vigorous exercise.

Also, rest assured, none of these stretches are girlie-man stretches done by a sissified, skinny wimp with a ballerina build. These are stretches that anyone can do. Even someone with a stocky, bulldog muscular build like mine. Even someone who is stiff as a board. Just watch the video and follow along and your muscles will begin to loosen; tension will melt away and your athletic skills will soar.

The second video will cover what I call ***Deep Breathing Stretches***. Once again, there are courses on deep breathing and there are courses on stretching, but mine is the only one that truly teaches you the most important keys about how to connect the two. Yes, you learn deep breathing techniques with some stretching programs, but mine cuts to the bone and shows you the **"master keys"** that make your breathing COMMAND your body to get more flexible.

Yes, I'll show you how to do the splits, but realize that this stretch is grossly over-rated. Think of your body as a complete system of energy. If your hip flexors and groin are flexible, that's only part of your body. If you want the real keys to flexibility, vitality and high energy, then you gotta get to work on your spine. That's where your personal electricity gets turned on. And that's where your energy gets blocked.

It's All About Vibration

Remember that your success in life is in direct proportion to how vibrant you are. And how do you increase your level of vibration, and rapidly? You do it through deep breathing, proper thinking and the most beneficial stretches to your entire system. Isolating one little muscle here and there is not what you want, especially in a combat situation. Your body moves as one unit. So don't stretch it one unit at a time. Do stretches that hit multiple areas of the body simultaneously. Do stretches that also, through the application of deep breathing and proper thinking, increase your physical strength and health. Again, you're not just going for flexibility. You're going for the entire package.

Tape three in the course teaches **Energy Drills & Joint Mobility Stretches.** ***And look out. We're talking major league great stuff here.***

For example, did you know that there are many exercises that martial artists, combat athletes and other exercise enthusiasts do, and without realizing it, they are literally harming themselves? **Why is it that more and more karate students need reconstructive knee surgery? Why is it that so many are having hip replacements?** Why is it that after the age of 40, many of the top karate kickers in the world, even those who used to have beautiful, powerful kicks—now have kicks that have literally turned to shit?

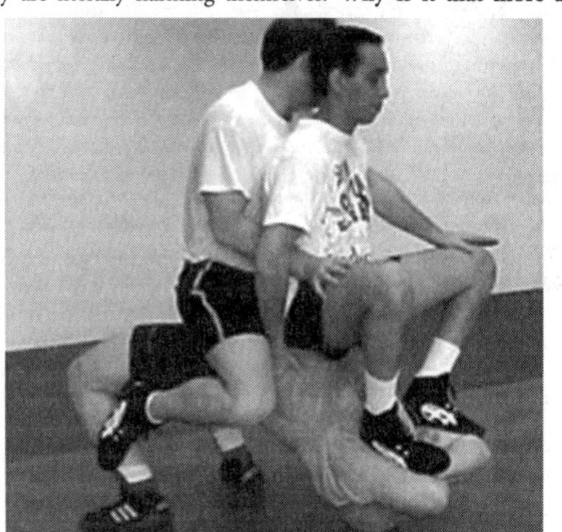

Matt Furey shows off his incredible flexibility by supporting two, adult men in a back-bridge

The flexibility of your spine is FAR more important than the splits

You'll find out why in this tape, and you'll learn some quick, simple, easy-to-learn energy drills I learned in China that will correct these weaknesses instantly. **Minutes after doing these drills, you're going to have greater flexibility and power in your lower limbs.** You're also going to be fired up, full of pep and enthusiasm that had inexplicably drained out of you, without you even knowing it.

In addition to this, you'll find another 15 exercises on this tape that loosen every joint in your body. Just doing these drills and joint loosening exercises, even without the other stretches, will astound you. You'll feel like a little kid again, bouncing off the walls with energy.

By now you should definitely see how much these tapes can help you. But I want to go one step further.

Normally this course will sell for $177 or more, but for a limited time, I will offer this course for $50 off, which drops the price to an unbelievably low $127 plus $8 S&H (foreign orders add $20 for S&H).

But that's not all.

Order now, and while supplies last, I'll also throw in a **free copy** of a tape called, ***"Chinese Underground Sports Rejuvenation Secrets" – a $199 dollar value.*** On this tape I am going to teach you what I learned on my last visit to our second home in China. These incredible techniques will, without a doubt, double your flexibility in record time. Not only that, they can help your aches, pains and injuries heal much faster. Learn the secret of how I eliminated Vampiro's shoulder problem inside of six minutes. Learn much, much more than that, too.

Order ***Combat Stretching – How To Double Your Flexibility In One Evening*** right now. Pick up the phone and call 813 994 8267 and place your order on our secure voicemail or place your order online at www.mattfurey.com. You can also mail your order to: Matt Furey, 10339 Birdwatch Dr., Tampa FL 33647.

Best,

Matt Furey

Matt Furey

P.S. Remember, for a limited time, if you order now, you'll get $50 off the regular price of $177 – dropping it to an incredibly low $127. Plus you'll get a free copy of ***"Chinese Underground Sports Rejuvenation Secrets" – valued at $199.*** Order now. Before this offer changes.

☐ Yes, Matt Please rush me the ***Combat Stretching – How To Double Your Flexibility In One Evening*** for only $127.00 plus $8 S&H. Plus, I'm eligible to receive a free copy of ***Chinese Underground Sports Rejuvenation Secrets*** while supplies last.

NAME: ____________________

ADDRESS: ____________________

CITY ________ STATE ________ ZIP ________

COUNTRY: ________ PHONE: ________

☐ Money Order drawn from a U.S. bank

☐ Visa ☐ MasterCard ☐ Amex ☐ Discover

CARD NO: ____________________

EXP: ________ SIGNATURE: ________

Make Money Order Payable to:

Matt Furey Enterprises, Inc.

10339 Birdwatch Dr., Tampa, Florida 33647, USA

www.mattfurey.com

Phone: (813) 994-8267 • **Fax:** (813) 994-4947

CmbtCndtn

"How to Become an Overnight Success"

Of course, there's no such thing. Or is there? Truth is, once you learn how to make a simple "shift" in your thinking – your life can instantly change for the better. It did for me and I believe it can for you as well.

by Matt Furey

Matt Furey demonstrates his Chi control.

In February of 1981, I was at the high school wrestling tournament in Des Moines, Iowa, trying to mentally prepare for my match in the state finals. I was a senior. This was the last match of my high school career. I had already beaten the defending state champion. I had already beaten the number three ranked man. Now it was down to two men and the best man was supposed to win.

But the best man didn't know how to use his mind when it counted. He didn't believe in himself. He didn't believe he deserved to win. He thought of himself as a nobody from a nobody town. This was his first trip to the state tournament. He came in unranked and unknown. He was out of his league. Hell, he was happy JUST to be in the finals. That was more than anyone from his area had expected.

You guessed it. I lost that match. I lost to a junior by one lousy point. I was devastated; not so much because I lost; but because I would have won – if I "would have" given my all. But I didn't give my ALL because I didn't know how to, on command, direct and govern my mind and INTERNAL FORCES.

The Night I Won a National Title and Became an "Overnight Success"

Four years later, in March of 1985, I was in the stands "mentally preparing" once again. This time it was for a crack at the national championship. As I sat in the stands my mind turned negative. It was déjà vu all over again. I was on a downward spiral that would end with me taking home yet another 2nd place medal.

The "Shift"

After several minutes of wallowing in negativity, I made a mental shift. I made a choice to leave the stands, to get out of the place where I couldn't concentrate. I went to a quiet room and closed my eyes. I breathed deeply and pictured myself as a champion – but in a way that I had never done so before.

30 minutes later, when I took the mat for the finals, I was a different man. I was NOT the same person who was full of fear, self-doubt and worry. And guess what? I walked away as "national champion."

Now, before you start thinking that I had the entire mental process of success down at that point, think again.

Yes, I knew how to use my mind better than when I did in high school – but I was still a long way off from knowing the real success secrets that I know and use today.

Matt does the unimaginabale and wins a World Shuai-chiao kung fu title in China.

From Nobody to World Champion

In December of 1997, twelve and a half years after winning a national collegiate title, I was in the stands in Beijing, China, mentally preparing for the gold medal round in the World Shuai-chiao kung fu championships. This time my barrels were fully loaded in terms of mental and physical skills. But even so, I found myself moving back and forth from images of winning the gold to dreadful thoughts of getting my ass kicked.

Once I recognized the negative emotion trying to take hold of me, I moved to another corner of the arena and did some deep breathing exercises. I inhaled positive energy and exhaled negative – and within a few minutes my mind was focused like a laser. I was clear about my purpose and 100% free of fear.

20 minutes later I accomplished the "impossible." I beat the Chinese and Mongolian national champion at his own game. I became the first and only American to ever win a World Shuia-chiao kung fu title in China.

How did I make the mental shift to accomplish my objective? By taking mind power techniques from the west and combining them with Chinese chi kung and relaxation teachings (my wife is from China and we have a vacation home there, on Hainan Island).

Upon my return to the U.S. in January of 1998, I began to focus on other areas of my life; areas that I had neglected while I was a competitive athlete, and without exception, every single area that I concentrated on improved.

And I can teach you how to create the same sort of success in your life, too. But before I do, let me ask:

Has anyone else ever pulled you aside and taught you about ***Magnetic Mind Power*** – and how you can use it to achieve whatever you want in life?

I doubt it.

How do I know? I know because I've spent the better part of my life, some 24 years learning about and researching the subject of mind power, in China and in the U.S. I've gone from being a lousy wrestler to a world champion. I've gone from being a wanna-be writer to a best-selling author. I've gone from living in poverty to becoming a multi-millionaire. And I'm improving by the day because I now know how to cut right to the meat of the matter.

The Secret Power of Chi

Everyone knows the Chinese have a recorded history that goes back at least 5,000 years. And everyone has heard about the mysterious powers the Chinese martial artists have developed.

But I'm willing to bet that no one has ever told you HOW to use this ***Chi*** power and direct it into

...come an Overnight Success" (continued)

...ne has ever taught you ...AGNETIC, and that when ...will not only improve your athletic ... also your health, your business and ...thing else in your life; including your sex life.

I Offer You the Power to Change Your Life

Perhaps you're wondering what I can do for you. Perhaps you're thinking: "Hey, all this success Furey has achieved is great for **HIM** – but what about me?"

Good question. Here's my answer:

I now offer you ***Magnetic Mind Power*** – power over your circumstances – ability to fascinate others – strength to make the good things happen for you the same way that a magnet draws bits of steel.

I offer you rugged individuality – that quality which makes you stand out from the crowd, no longer timid and self-conscious, but a ***man's man... (or woman's woman!)***

I offer you a new personality, supreme confidence, and the magnetic power to achieve anything you desire.

I offer you SUCCESS – in sports, in business, in academics, in life itself. I offer you the ability to dominate – the ability to get what you want!

***Magnetic Mind Power* is the human being's most powerful force. It is more powerful than electricity because electricity doesn't think for itself. It doesn't decide upon something and make it happen. It doesn't attract the circumstances it wants. Electricity just IS. Magnetic Mind Power is far more than that.**

Its possibilities are startling – almost unreal. Deep down within you, woven into the very fiber of your being lies this power. It is sleeping. **And it will sleep forever unless you arouse it!**

I can awaken the ***Magnetic Mind Power*** within you and I can do it almost overnight – but only if you're the type of person who is open to a mental "shift."

Once you make the "shift" you will begin harnessing and using the magnetic power within you that moves your goals closer to you and you closer to your goals. You will attract new and better circumstances into your life. You will find yourself on the road to a wonderful self-confidence and a feeling of personal power. You will hold the **KEY** that unlocks the door to achieving anything you want in life.

This "overnight shift" will be the greatest in your life because it is the beginning of the **NEW YOU**. In just one evening you can change your mind, your way of thinking ... and ultimately **YOUR LIFE**.

Magnetic Mind Power is not limited to a "fortunate few." It is Nature's gift to everybody. The secret lies in knowing and applying a few fundamental **LAWS**.

By knowing, understanding and most importantly, applying, these LAWS, your life will work out the way you want it to. By ignoring them, your life will work out the way you fear. The choice is yours entirely.

What is Magnetic Mind Power?

No doubt you have secretly envied people who possess that magic quality to achieve whatever they set their mind on. Consider the famous athletes or business people you admire. Which one attracts you, grips you, thrills you, compels your admiration? That one has it – ***Magnetic Mind Power***! He has the ability to attract what he wants in life like steel to a magnet.

Now consider yourself... Do people always remember you? Do you fascinate and thrill and quite possibly cause envy to those around you? Do people remember your name and face? Do folks exclaim: *"Everything he does just seems to turn out right. He's so lucky."*

Or are you just one of the crowd – timid, weak-voiced, ordinary – plugging along – getting nowhere?

Wake up, my friend! That's no way to live. Be somebody, act alive, show folks you stand for something. Electrify your friends with your new-born, full grown ***Magnetic Mind Power***.

Results Seen Instantly

With ***Magnetic Mind Power*** you'll lose all fear. All timidity. All awkwardness. You'll gain supreme self-confidence. You'll be given an altogether different outlook on life – instantly. You'll become a clear-cut personality. You'll be given an almost uncanny power to get what you want in life. And with the great power in your hands, you will go thru life supremely happy – reaping the glowing rewards of success.

Now, here's a quick look at what you'll learn in the *Magnetic Mind Power* system:

- **How to build unshakeable self-confidence!**
- The Chinese word 'yi' and how you can use it to bring about dramatic changes in your life!
- **The role imagination, emotion and action play in making your goals become a reality.**
- The Chinese saying, "Better to be born lucky than smart," and how you can manufacture luck on command!
- **Why you should always think of everything you do as easy, even if it is difficult?**
- Powerful ways to direct your mind to your target so that you always achieve it
- **The Chinese belief in the power of words on paper and how this relates to your success**
- What to do whenever you encounter set-backs or obstacles
- **How to calm your mind and let it work for you while your body rests**
- How your subconscious will deliver the answers you need to guarantee your success
- **"Thick Face-Black Heart" – The Chinese belief on single-minded focus as well as immunity to criticism and why these are the hallmarks of the super successful person**
- The role deep breathing plays in helping you attain your desires
- **Why "mental work" should never be strenuous**
- The principle of the "Inner Smile" and why this single skill puts you on the winner's track
- **Simple ways to rid yourself of nervousness, fear, anxiety or worry, especially when you feel it prior to an important event**

What's in the Magnetic Mind Power system?

The ***Magnetic Mind Power*** system was originally created for athletes and martial artists – but shortly after making it available, people involved in every imaginable pursuit started buying it and later, telling me how much it helped them get a better job, make more money, improve relationships, and so on.

The entire system is composed of 2 "private" DVD's that were shot from my very own living room – as well as 2 audio CD's that you'll have playing in your car all day long. In addition to the above, you'll receive a workbook that highlights all the essential parts of the program. As a package, you'll find everything taking you to the next level of success.

Magnetic Mind Power is only $147 plus $10 S&H ($20 S&H foreign). But I have something else very special that I'd like to send you in addition to this course.

How to Get My Dynamic Deep Breathing DVD FREE

As an added bonus, if you're one of the first 50 people to order ***Magnetic Mind Power*** I'll send you my ***Dynamic Deep Breathing DVD*** (a $69 value) absolutely FREE. In this DVD I reveal the entire sequence of Chinese and old-time American dynamic deep breathing exercises I do each day. I have previously taught a couple of these dynamic deep breathing exercises, but never the entire sequence along with incredibly important details that will immediately increase your levels of magnetic power .

Don't delay. Fill in the coupon seen below – then mail or **FUREY FAX** it to us at 813 994 4947. You can also phone your order into our secure voicemail system at 813 994 8267.

☐ Yes, send me the ***Magnetic Mind Power course*** for only $147 plus $10 S&H ($20 S&H foreign). Plus, as an added bonus, I'll receive your ***Dynamic Deep Breathing DVD*** just for ordering now.

NAME: ______________________

ADDRESS: ______________________

CITY ____________ STATE ____________ ZIP ____________

COUNTRY: ____________ PHONE: ____________

☐ Money Order drawn from a U.S. bank

☐ Visa ☐ MasterCard ☐ Amex ☐ Discover

CARD NO: ______________________

EXP: ____________ SIGNATURE: ____________

Make Money Order Payable to:

Matt Furey Enterprises, Inc.
10339 Birdwatch Dr., Tampa, Florida 33647, USA
www.mattfurey.com
Phone: (813) 994-8267 • **Fax:** (813) 994-4947

CmbtCndtn

Other Matt Furey Books and Courses

available at www.mattfurey.com

____ *Combat Conditioning Book* $29.95

____ *Kick Ass – Take Names...*
Confessions of a Fitness and Fighting Guru $29.95

____ *Gama Fitness* $197.00

____ *The Furey Fat Loss System CD* $39.00

____ *Combat Conditioning Videos* $129.00

____ *Combat Cardio CD* $39.00

____ *Extreme Flexibility Secrets of The Chinese Acrobats* $69.00

____ *Combat Stretching* $127.00

____ *Combat Abs Book* $29.95

____ *The Secret Power of Handstand Training* $79.00

____ *Farmer Burns Catch Wrestling Home Study Course* $597.00

____ *Farmer Burns 1914 Classic –*
Lessons in Wrestling & Physical Culture $35.00

____ *Street Grappling* $99.00

____ *Neck Cranks* $69.00

____ *The Martial Art of Wrestling* $39.95

____ *Combat Training – The Road to China* $49.00

____ *How To Hook A Heavyweight Without Flopping to the Guard* $49.00

____ *How To Escape Any Submission Hold* – Volume One $49.00

____ *How To Cut Weight For Wrestling Without Losing Strength* $29.95

Total for page:____________

____ ***Shuai-chiao Takedown Tactics for Grapplers*** $49.00

____ ***Mongolian Grappling Secrets Revealed*** – Two Videos $69.00

____ ***How To Use Your Feet To Score Takedowns*** $49.00

____ ***How to Eliminate Carpal Tunnel Syndrome within 30 Days*** $97

____ ***Magnetic Mind Power*** $149.00

____ ***Unrevealed Secrets of Man*** by George F. Jowett $29.95

____ ***Chuang Shang de Gong Fu*** $297.00

____ ***How to Make $1,000,000 (One Million) per Year (or More) As A Personal Trainer or Fitness Professional*** $1,000.00

Total from prev page:____________

Subtotal:____________

S&H:____________

Total:____________

NAME: ________________________

ADDRESS: ________________________

CITY: ____________ STATE/PROVINCE: ____________

ZIP/POSTAL CODE: ____________

PHONE: ____________ FAX: ____________

EMAIL: ____________

- ❑ Money Order
- ❑ Visa ❑ MasterCard ❑ Amex ❑ Discover

CARD NO: ____________

EXP: ________ SIGNATURE: ____________

Make Money Order Payable to:

Matt Furey Enterprises, Inc.

10339 Birdwatch Dr., Tampa, Florida 33647, USA • **Phone:** (813) 994-8267 • **Fax:** (813) 994-4947

For a complete list of products, visit: **www.mattfurey.com**

<u>"FREE Fitness Newsletter and CD"</u>

We'd love to send <u>YOU</u> a free issue of the ***Matt Furey Inner Circle*** monthly CD and newsletter. Furey's extraordinary knowledge on fitness and success pours off every page of the newsletter. And the CD literally walks and talks you through an exceptional do-at-home or do-on-the-road workout each month. Follow along with Matt as he helps you get into the best shape of your life.

Here's what to do: Fill in the order blank below and **FUREY FAX** to 813 994 4947.

Or send by mail to:

Gold Medal Publications, Inc.
10339 Birdwatch Drive
Tampa, FL 33657

Name: ____

Address: ____

City: ______________________ **State/Province:** ________________

Zip/Postal Code: ______________

Phone: ______________________ **FAX:** ____________________

email: ________________________

website: ______________________

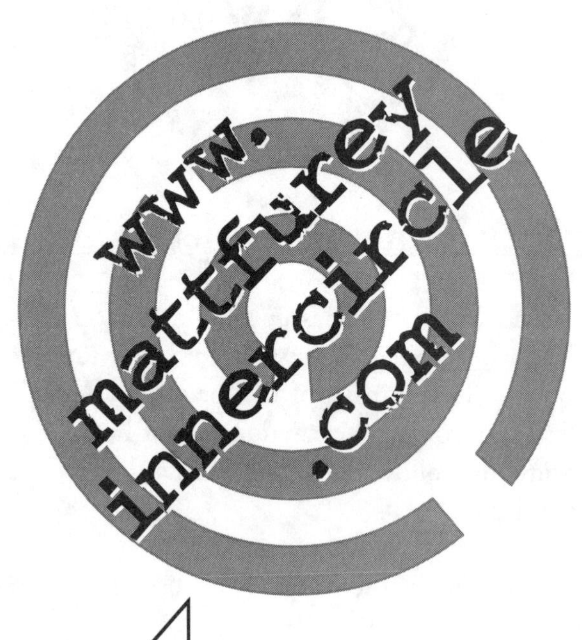

Turn back to page 143 to find out how you can receive a FREE newsletter and CD from *Matt Furey's Inner Circle*.